To Barbara
A wonderful
is a great role
I'm sure she'll read, learn, enjoy
and share the contents of this book.
I'm looking forward to hearing your
feedback.

'A wonderful life?'

By
Keef Feeley

Have a wonderful retirement

Keef

keeffeeley@hotmail.co.uk

Book Description
"A Wonderful Life?" by Keef Feeley
ISBN 978-1-906905-09-5
Page Verso

"A Wonderful Life?"

Cormorant Publishing Hartlepool

Copyright holder   K. Feeley

Subtitle: n/a

Author: Keef Feeley

First published in 2009 by Cormorant Publishing Hartlepool, 5 Teesdale Avenue, Hartlepool, Cleveland, TS26 9QD.
www.riddlewrites.co.uk
Copyright © K. Feeley The author has asserted his moral rights.

ISBN 978-1-906905-09-5

Production Manager: John Riddle

Cover design: Cormorant Publishing Hartlepool Design Team

Printed and bound in the UK by Connoisseur Crafts, Hartlepool Enterprise Centre, Brougham Terrace, Hartlepool TS24 8EY.
Concrafts@surfree.co.uk

Acknowledgements

This book is the result of over thirty years of observing, listening and trying to help thousands of young people cope and succeed towards the end of the 20th century and the start of the 21st. I would like to thank the huge contribution of my wife and her children, my first wife and our children, my brothers and sister and their children, my friends and their children, and also the thousands of pupils that enriched my life at Marshalls Park, Boswells and Sir Charles Lucas schools.

Contents

Chapter 1
The Beginning or The End?

"Why do you keep doing this to us, don't you care? Stacey's furious mother shouts at her as they arrive home from the police station. "What's your reason this time for hitting that girl?"
"She called me 'booby', she knows I hate that name!" Stacey manages to reply.
 Her father joins in. "What do you expect, if you go out dressed like that! You always go out with your tits and arse on view! What do we do now? Do you know or even care how this has affected your mother?"
"This is my best clubbing gear" Stacey answers.
"Clubbing! You look like a whore! Don't you have any self respect?" He responds.
Stacey is too upset (and hung-over) to reply.
"What have we done to deserve it". He adds
"You've just caused us one problem after another. Why? What have we done to deserve this?" He repeats.
Stacey runs up to her bedroom, 'crying her eyes out' and throws herself onto her bed, her arrest for assaulting a girl at a night club is just too much to bare, and she feels at the age of nineteen she's had just a succession of problems and frustration. She now feels as though she's at the bottom of a deep pit and it's impossible to climb out, and the more she tries, the more slippery the sides become.
Stacey can think of only one solution – 'alcohol' and digs out the bottle of vodka she has hidden away and starts to drink it straight from the bottle. It's been a long time since Stacey last ate anything

so the neat vodka has a very rapid effect. For some strange reason, the words her dad had said began swimming around her head.

"What've we done to deserve this, what've we done to deserve this,"

She realises it's one of her dad's favourite songs and searches for it on her i-pod. She finds it quite quickly, it's by a group called the 'Pet Shop Boys' and it's actually called "What've I done to deserve this" which makes it seem even more relevant, so she puts it on 'repeat' and sticks on her headphones.

Unfortunately, the vodka and the song only serves to make her feel more unhappy and remorseful, she begins to cry profusely, reflecting on her years of problems, the desperate situation she now feels she's in and the harm she has caused her family.

A voice in her head says to her,

"This world is much too cruel to live in, your life is worthless and everyone would be better off without you, and there is no point in carrying on."

She gets the box of paracetamol out of the drawer and swallows the lot, washing them down with the last few drops of vodka.

"What have I, what have I, what have I done to deserve this", was ringing in Stacey ears as she felt herself slowly slipping away.

Suddenly Stacey sensed she wasn't alone, and she slowly regained her consciousness.

A strange shape like a glowing snowman seemed to be standing at the bottom of her bed, as the mist in her eyes cleared, she could see it was actually an old man. He had white hair, was clean shaven and wore an old fashioned black suit.

"Who are you, what you doing here" she said loudly, almost shouting,

"Don't you recognise me, look at me closely" he said calmly.

Stacey stared at him; "You do look familiar, where have I seen you before"

"Well you haven't actually seen me in person, but you've seen my picture many times, on your parents wall in the living room" he replied.

"Granddad Arthur!" she yelled, "My mum's granddad".

"That's right, well remembered" was Arthur response.

"But you died before I was born" Stacey said with a puzzled look on her face.

Arthur answered, "That could be true, it depends on what you mean by dead, if you mean dead to be the human body no longer functions, then you're right, but if you mean no longer existing then you're wrong".

"Dead is dead, what are you going on about?" Stacey said impatiently.

Arthur replies, "Do I look dead to you?"

"Well no, but I could be dreaming or you could just look like my mum's granddad, or …" Stacey paused for a moment.

"Or I could be dead!" Arthur answers. "They are all possibilities. Perhaps I can help you understand. Do you recall seeing films at Christmas called 'It's a Wonderful Life' and A Christmas Carol?"

"Yes, of course I do, they're my mum's favourite films, we've had to watch them every year. Why, what's that got to do with anything?" Stacey grunted.

"Well apart from being shown at Christmas, did they have anything in common?" Arthur asked.

After a short pause, Stacey replied.

"They both had ghosts or angel type people in them, who showed them what their lives were like, or something like that."

Arthur did not respond immediately, Stacey's face slowly showed a glimmer of realisation.

"Are you trying to tell me that you are a ghost or an angel?" Stacey asked.

"Well it depends on what you mean by ghosts or angels" replied Arthur.

Stacey said. "I've no idea what ghosts or angels are, or if they even exist".

7

"In that case, think of me as a ghost or angel, more importantly, I'm here to try to help you and hopefully get you to help others" Arthur replied in his calm soothing tone.

"Help me and get me to help others, you're joking, how do you hope to do that", Stacey quickly replied in her typically rude tone.

Arthur answered, "In the same way that Clarence, the angel in 'It's a Wonderful Life' and the ghosts did with Scrooge, by developing your self-awareness".

"Developing my self-awareness, what does that mean?" Stacey asked.

Arthur explained "It's one of the essential skills we need in order to succeed, First I'm going to try and help you answer the question in the song 'What have I done to deserve this?" Arthur pointed to the i-pod, and the music became loud again.

"How do you aim to do that, then?" Stacey again responded in her typical tone.

"In the same way as the angels or ghosts in the films", said Arthur, "by giving you a chance to study how your life could've been different if you'd developed the key skills you need to succeed"

"What are these 'key skills you need to succeed', that you keep going on about, I've never heard of them, I don't know what you mean", Stacey responded, clearly getting frustrated.

Arthur detected her frustration and pointed to the wall to his right and Stacey's left, "There they are, I'll explain them to you" he said. Stacey looked to where Arthur was pointing, and suddenly the whole wall was covered with writing, as if a slide was being shone on it. Her jaw dropped, the back of her neck tingled, she was amazed and confused, "how did he do that" she thought, but was too stunned to say anything, if she hadn't been sitting on her bed, propped up by the headboard she would probably have keeled over.

Stacey stared at the wall and gradually read it.

The skills we need to succeed

Effective Learning
Communication
Cognitive (thinking)
Self-awareness
Managing Feelings
Motivation
Empathy
Social skills

"What does it mean?" Stacey finally managed to speak, and was now feeling a little frightened.

Arthur explained, "When humans are born they are weak and very dependent on others to help them survive, but they are extremely good at learning, which begins even before birth".

A video of a baby in the womb appeared on the wall, which illustrated his point.

Arthur continued. "Providing we learn the essential skills in our early years we can not only survive but we can begin to overcome the difficulties we meet in life and become successful. Do you understand?"

"I don't know what you mean by skills". Stacey was actually listening and thinking about what he'd said, which she rarely did at school and college.

Arthur responded. "You are probably used to hearing about skills like learning to speak, or read, or write, even riding a bike or swimming, it means activities that you learn how to do. We are not born able to do these things, 'these skills', because we need to learn how to do them. In the first few years of our lives, our brains are brilliant at learning if we provide the correct learning requirements, so we can start learning all of these skills if we get the opportunities".

Videos of young children playing and learning appeared on the wall, followed by an image of the inner workings of the brain, emphasised his point.

"So are you saying that if I'd developed these skills, my life would've been different and I wouldn't have had so many problems and frustrations?" asked Stacey.

"I am" said Arthur, "and we're going to watch a film, or video or something similar, with you in the starring role".

"Well, it won't take much for it to be a better life than this one" Stacey said after thinking for a moment. "And you're going to do this to help me?"

"That's the aim, and hopefully get you to help others" Arthur replied.

"That ain't gonna be easy, so lets get started" Stacey mumbled as she adjusted her position and propped herself up on her bed in readiness.

Arthur continued, "You're probably right, but my role is to at least try, and we'll begin in the same way as in 'A Christmas Carol', by looking at your past." He pointed at the wall. "Do you recognise that little girl?"

"That's me!" Stacey yelled. "That looks to be about eight years ago, I'm wearing my school uniform, it looks brand new."

"It is you, this is your first day at secondary school, and you don't look very happy". Arthur commented.

"I'm not surprised, I had been dreading that day for a long time", Stacey said.

Arthur replied "That's obvious if we listen to what you're saying".
Sound started to come out of the video on the wall.

"It's going to be horrible, I know it is. I don't know anybody." The young Stacey moaned.

Arthur commented on what she'd heard. "Actually over a dozen children from your class in primary school were starting there on the same day, but you didn't get on with any of them, because of your poor development of the eight essential skills. Your mother is attempting to make you feel better, but as you can see, you weren't making much of an effort. You had not really enjoyed primary school and the prospect of going to secondary school had been haunting you for months."

Arthur continued his commentary on the video, "Here, you and your mother are walking to your new school, and your mum is pushing your sister Suzi, in a pushchair, she is about 18 months old here. If you study your attitude in this scene, it may illustrate your poorly developed skills, to you."

Sound then again came from the scene on the wall.

"You'll be alright, everyone feels like you on their first day, you'll soon find a friend. Look, isn't that Tracey from your old school?" Stacey's mother asked.

"Yeah, it is. You can go now mum, I don't want them to see you, it's embarrassing having you walk to school with me, I'm not a little kid." Stacey snapped.

"Alright, alright. I understand, I mustn't spoil your image" Stacey's mother replied.

"OK, I'll see you after school, bye." Stacey said abruptly, and shot off towards Tracey, while her mother turned around the pushchair and started to return home with Suzi.

"Who's your tutor, Trace?" Stacey asked

"Miss Clark, she's really nice. Who's yours?" Tracey replied.

"Mr Brown, he's horrible, he's got 'four eyes' and a deep loud voice. I'm sure he picked on me when we had our day up here last term." Stacey moaned.

Arthur then commented "Your poor development of the essential skills explains your lack of confidence and negative attitude".

The next scene on the wall then showed young Stacey entering her new classroom with her tutor directing her to her seat.

"I knew it, I just knew he'd sit me next to someone I don't know". Stacey mumbled as she was sat down next to a little girl with blond curly hair.

The blond girl immediately introduced herself. "Hello my name is Lucy".

"I'm Stace' replied Stacey abruptly.

Arthur explained. "Although Lucy correctly thought you were being rude and aggressive she didn't get upset, she proceeded to try to get to know you by politely asking a number of questions. Unfortunately, your lack of skills made you uncomfortable and reluctant to tell people about yourself. Furthermore, you didn't feel particularly interested in getting to know Lucy, despite Lucy's enthusiasm. Therefore, when lunchtime finally arrived, you shot off to find Tracey and your friends from your 'old school'. The first day seemed to go on forever you, because your poor skill development meant you felt so inadequate. This next scene shows you walking home with your 'old friends from primary school', again displaying your lack of skills with these negative comments."

"What a bloody awful day" The young Stacey in the video grumbled. "I was sat next to a girl who never stopped talking and asking me questions. Everything is so confusing, what's that timetable all about? I can't see me ever being able to work it out and I don't know how many times I got lost, the school is like a giant maze. Everyone is continually shouting at you and telling you what to do all the time!"

The girls all agreed with her and continued moaning all the way home, which seemed to take forever as they'd all found the day so tiring and difficult.

When Stacey finally got home her mother was keen to find out about the day.

"So how was it? Her mother asked.

"Alright" Stacey replied as she plonked herself down in front of the television. Her mum took this to mean 'back off, I don't want to talk about it'. Stacey switched on the TV and decided to just try and forget about the day, luckily a few 'soaps', that she watched all the time came on and 'gave her other things to think about'.

Arthur again commented.

"This also shows your poor skills, as your communication with your mother is so poor, you are unable to talk about or manage your feelings. We are going to continue to watch your story, and your descent down the slippery slope into the pit of despair you are now in because of these poorly developed skills. I will then illustrate how different your life could've been if you'd learnt these essential skills, and hopefully it will convince you to start to try to learn these skills and overcome your problems."

Arthur continued. "For you, the first week seemed to go on for ever, with each day getting worse and worse as they seemed to get more and more difficult. You kept 'getting lost' and forgot something everyday and by the end of the week you had become 'thoroughly cheesed off with all the hassle'. In this next scene, your father tried to help you but your poor development of managing your feelings prevented it occurring."

The voice of Stacey's father came from the wall.

"So how's the first week been then Stace?"

"Worst week of my life" she replied.

"Why's that then?" He responded."Everybody shouts at you all the time, I don't know what the teachers are on about, the stuff they expect us to do is far too hard, I can't do it and nobody helps you." Stacey complained.

"Everyone feels like that when they start secondary school, you'll soon get over it." He replied.

"Huh!" responded Stacey and she stormed off to her bedroom in a huff.

Arthur then explained.

"In the space of six weeks, you went from having just one teacher in primary school to at least 8 different teachers in secondary school. Almost everyone finds it difficult to concentrate and understand all of them. Unfortunately, your poor self awareness meant that you thought, 'everyone else seems O.K.' and you were embarrassed by your inability to cope, so you pretended you were 'O.K.' to your classmates and teachers."

"After a few weeks into the term it was clear that homework was a big problem for you, you didn't know how to do some of it or how long to spend on it, so you either spent hours on it or gave up almost straightaway. When your parents asked about it you had a few quick answers, to hide the truth.

'They didn't give us any'.

'The teacher was absent'

'I did it in class.'

'I can't do this because we haven't done any of this in class'.

'It's too difficult, I can't do it."

Arthur continues,

"These last two statements began to cause problems for you, because your parents' response was to put pressure on you to ask the teachers for help, or worse still, they were going to contact the school about it. Your poor self awareness meant you believed that these two suggestions indicated that you were 'thick' because you couldn't do it and everyone else could (not true, of course, but you thought so) and your mates would think that you put a high value on schoolwork and studying."

"Mr. Brown, your tutor, had realised you were struggling and discussed his concerns with you, but since you were so poor at managing your feelings you did nothing to apply his excellent advice and support. Unfortunately, your poor social skills meant you didn't like or understand many of your teachers and classmates, so as a way of coping you showed little interest in the lessons and became increasingly annoyed with these people."

"However you did manage to find some new friends, Sharon ('Shazza') and Charlotte ('Charlie') as they appeared to feel the same way as you about teachers and classmates. So you spent much of your time complaining to each other about the 'useless teachers', 'the boring lessons' and 'the boffs' (the classmates you didn't get on with)."

"Your poor empathy and social skills meant that you were desperate to find friends with a similar attitude to yours, as it helped you feel more comfortable and more able to ignore the difficulties you were experiencing. This attitude extended to the various after-school clubs and activities that were offered at secondary school, so you and these friends decided not to go to them. You felt that you were no good at sport, music, drama or dance and you would be 'shown up and laughed at' if you went to them, so you avoided them and claimed 'they're really for boffs anyway".

Arthur continued his explanation of the scenes shown on the wall.

"Your friends also lacked these essential skills, so you supported each other in your negative attitudes.

You had not particularly enjoyed primary school, but managed to cope, but studying and learning in class in secondary school was much more difficult. You and your new friends' solution was to avoid the difficulties with 'idle chatter, gossip and taking the p***', so gaining a reputation as 'Chatterboxes'. Being grouped with these girls bonded you together and you felt accepted by them as someone who is a 'good laugh' and 'has the bottle to stick up for herself'. You all had limited, but similar interests, such as meeting in town and shopping, watching similar TV programmes and films, with an increasing focus on fashion, 'teenage magazines' and boys".

"Your common cries at school are 'he hates me' and 'he's always picking on me'. Your growing reputation for 'chatter and disrupting lessons' meant the teachers 'kept a close eye on you' to try to stop these events occurring, so frequently spotted you misbehaving".

Stacey, sitting upright on her bed, was listening more intently than she'd ever done before and was fascinated at watching her life appear on the wall.

"I've never thought about any of this before, but it seems to make sense". She said.

Arthur resumed his commentary to the 'video on the wall'.

"As the weeks passed, you increasingly felt that many of your lessons were too difficult and 'not worth the effort', which in turn increased the occasions when you got 'told off' for being late, or not doing homework, or 'talking in class'. You and your new friends did not get on with most of the rest of the class and spent a lot of time calling them names and 'picking on them'. Your new friends are about the only thing you liked about secondary school. After a few months, you and your friends began to argue repeatedly, causing you to keep 'falling out' and then 'making up'. The poor development of your managing feelings and social skills meant that you and your friends didn't really know or trust each other."

"At home, your parents have started to worry about your lack of interest in your studies and the meagre quantity and quality of homework you do. However, when they ask you about it the replies they receive from you are:

'Get off my back'

'You're stressing me out'

'You're always moaning at me'

Barely a day goes by without an argument with your parents, frequently ending up as a 'shouting match'. As you can see by the typical scene on the wall, you are reluctant to get up in the morning and you are making less and less effort to be in school on time."

"Another persistent problem for you is Maths, you never liked the subject, but you now 'hate the teacher' and believe that 'he hates you' and is far too strict, mainly because he won't let you sit and talk to your friends! Eventually, you decided to truant, slipping out at the start of the last lesson of the day. Remarkably, you didn't get caught, and your friends thought you've 'got real bottle', as they put it, to have done it."

"Your poorly developed self awareness, managing feelings and motivation skills meant that you and your friends placed a high value on negative activities."

Stacey interrupted at this point and asked.

"What do you mean 'a high value on negative activities?"

Arthur replied.

"Basically, your poor development of these skills means you have 'low self esteem' and so are continually searching for ways to make you feel valued or important. Since learning new skills is too slow and difficult for you, you decided to focus on the easier option of risk taking and putting down other people, such as bullying and gossip."

"A good example of this, is that on one occasion on your way home from school with your mates, you were offered a cigarette by one of your friends, and although you'd vowed 'I will never smoke as it killed my grandad', all the others took one and you could not resist. Of course, it is not long before this becomes a common occurrence for you and your friends."

"As the year progressed, you and your friends became extremely interested in 'how you looked', especially hair and fashion. Teenage magazines became your 'bible', determining what you should wear, how you should behave and who you should like and dislike. Boys, either in the magazines or in school became your major topic of conversation and the most looked forward to event is the 'school disco'. As you can see on the wall, a very significant event for you occurred at this disco when you had your first 'real snog', as you continually referred to it, with Adam Firth, a year 8 boy. Not only was this a night you never forgot, you used it to make your friends extremely jealous!"

Stacey commented on this.

"You're right, I do remember that night very clearly, and I suppose I did use it to wind up my mates."

Arthur carried on.

"But this 'snog' was to lead to much more as you and your friends then began to go to the park on Friday afternoons after school to meet Adam Firth, Steven Smith and their friends 'to have a laugh'. Your lack of other interests meant you really enjoyed these events a great deal and within a few weeks you began to drink alcohol there along with the others. The feeling of confidence due to the loss of inhibition that the alcohol provided, caused you to be even more of a 'show off' than usual, so that the others thought you were amusing, though they were probably actually laughing at you. Furthermore, this 'loss of inhibition' from the alcohol influenced another negative activity, on your way home from the park you went into a clothes shop and shoplifted a 'top'. Unfortunately your mates and the boys are impressed by this act, interpreting this risky behaviour as having 'bottle', encouraging you to repeat it in the future."

Seeing these activities on the 'wall' actually embarrassed Stacey.

The pictures then shifted to Stacey's parents receiving a letter requesting them to attend an interview at the school, to discuss her 'Attendance and Behaviour'.

Arthur's commentary recommenced.

"Although your parents, were aware that you had struggled to adjust and cope with your first year at secondary school, it wasn't until this interview they discovered the extent of your difficulties. Both Mr Brown, your tutor, and Mrs Clark, your Head of Year, point out that 'although you clearly have ability, it is your poor attitude that seems to be the problem' and it is agreed by all four adults that you will get 'extra support' in future. This conversation when you and you parents get home, again reflects your poor self awareness and low self esteem"

From the video on the wall Stacey's father could clearly be heard asking.

"Why have you been getting into so much trouble, why didn't you tell us you were struggling?"

"I did, I've said loads of times, those teachers don't like me, they pick on me and won't help me. They only care about the boffs." Stacey replied.

"Well they said they are going to give you extra support now." Her mother responded.

"It won't be the sort of help I need, I bet. They'll just show me up in front of my mates or worse they'll send me to the 'unit for dummies'. I'm gonna look like a right thicko!" Stacey commented

"Well you've got exams coming up soon, you'll be able to show in those that you're not thick, won't you?" Her dad responded.

"Huh, I've got no chance of doing well, they haven't taught me anything all year, the teachers are rubbish." Stacey answered.

"You can't keep blaming the teachers Stacey, you've got to make the effort, Mr Brown and Mrs Clark both said it's your attitude that's the problem." Her mother commented.

"They're bound to say that aren't they. They ain't gonna say that the teachers are rubbish or they pick on me are they?" Stacey angrily replied.

"Well you'll have lots of time to revise for the exams as you are grounded until they've finished." Her father responded.

"I knew you'd take their side, you always do." Stacey said as she stormed off to her bedroom.

Arthur then interrupted this dialogue on the video.

"Looking for excuses and delegating blame, is a clear reflection of your poor self awareness and motivation skills."

"For the next few weeks you did some preparation for your exams, but since you don't really know what to do, and find it 'so boring', you struggled to do much effective learning. However, you consoled yourself by thinking and saying that 'it doesn't help much, anyway'. You showed as little interest as you could in school and the exams, thinking that you appeared 'cool' to your mates. No surprise therefore, that you did very poorly in the exams, claiming, of course, it was because you didn't revise. These poor exam results cause yet another argument with your parents, who 'ground' you for another two weeks."

"Throughout the summer holiday the arguments and groundings continued since you desperately wanted to spend most of the holiday 'hanging around' with your friends and 'boys' in various houses, the park, and shopping centres. These activities are both expensive and 'risky', as much of the time and money is spent on your appearance and 'fashion', repeatedly colouring and styling hair, studying and buying or stealing clothes, shoes, bags, jewellery, perfume, make up and accessories with 'the right label'. The visits to the park became more frequent and the smoking and drinking of alcohol became more excessive. Your repeated 'demands' for money to fund these activities also increased your arguments, as well as the nature of the activities themselves. Furthermore, your reluctance to help with any work in the home, or look after your little sister, and your continual moaning about being bored meant your relationships with your parents continued to deteriorate. All this is a clear illustration of your poorly developed motivation skill."

Chapter 2
Slipping Out Of Control

The 'video on the wall' now shows young Stacey in school, starting her second year.

Arthur explains.

"Your disappointing exam results meant you were placed in the lower sets but so are your friends, which meant you remained together for many lessons, allowing you to support each other's negative attitudes. Therefore, the new term continued much as the previous had ended, with you becoming even less interested in study and more focused on 'gossip' in lessons. At home, the relationship of you with your parents also continued to deteriorate and you spent most of your time at home in your bedroom watching TV and videos, listening to music, or communicating with your mates on the internet. As a result of these activities you went to sleep very late and struggled to wake up and get out of bed in the morning, causing you to be frequently late for school and sparking further arguments at home."

"You and your mates reputation as 'bullies' has grown due to your repeated criticisms and ridicule ('bitching') of other girls, often resulting in 'slanging matches' and 'vendettas'. Furthermore, you are now frequently being accused of threats and intimidation, both physical and emotional. These problems continue to spoil your relationship with your parents, and their only communication with you became frequent loud arguments. Your poor management of feelings meant that whenever, you were asked a question you replied aggressively and attempted to blame whoever you could for your problems, with your usual responses being;

'You just don't understand',
'Everyone else does it',
'They hate me',
'They're just dickheads'
'Don't treat me as if I'm a child'.
When you were at school or with your mates, you also blamed your parents."

"Your poor motivation skill meant you had a very limited range of interests, all of which tended to revolve around boys or your appearance in order to attract boys. You have become a regular reader of 'girls magazines', which focus mainly on celebrity, fashion, boys and sex, and they add to your obsession about your appearance. This obsession has become extremely expensive and you spend (and your mates) large sums of money on your appearance, and most of your time on it or talking about it or about boys and celebrities. Your social life now means going out to buy or steal things that might improve your appearance to attract boys or activities with boys. As well as spending a lot of money on your appearance such as labelled clothes, jewellery, hair, make up, tanning, you also spend a lot of time using your mobile phone and the internet to communicate to your friends and boys. Perhaps, you can see how narrow your life has become due to your poor social skills."

Stacey replies immediately.

"I can now! Watching your life as a movie gives you a chance to think about it, but I've never thought about it before."

As another scene of the younger Stacey arguing with her parents appears on the wall, Arthur continued his commentary.

"This very high expenditure resulted in further arguments with your parents. As well as suggesting you spend less, your parents suggested that you should be trying to get a part time job like delivering local papers, and here is your response."

The voice of young Stacey can now be heard from the video.

"I'm not doing those sort of jobs, you clearly don't understand how embarrassing that would be for me, I can't believe you would even suggest it. All the kids my age spend much more money than I do."

Arthur then explained.

"Your poor development of self awareness, managing feelings and motivation skills is illustrated by this comment and it demonstrates your low self esteem".

"At school, your poor learning skills meant you had not learnt from your poor performance in your first year at secondary school and your approach remained unchanged, apart from you becoming less interested. You continued to do as little study as you could get away with, either at school or at home, with almost no preparation for tests or exams, and you still had no idea what to do anyway. However, your poor results in the tests or exams are always accompanied with excuses such as;

'Didn't revise'

'We haven't done any of this'

'The teacher didn't tell us we had a test'

'They're a waste of time anyway'.

Although the Parents' consultation evenings at school in your first year were not very pleasant they have become increasingly difficult as the teachers complain so much about your attitude. Understandably perhaps, with so many difficulties of their own with you at home, your parents retaliated by complaining at the school's inability to get you to do any work. Having found this whole experience very uncomfortable and frustrating, they decided there is no useful purpose being served by going to these evenings so they stopped going."

"Unfortunately, your reputation for 'bitching and bullying' meant you became unpopular with many girls. In fact even your 'friends' became cautious around you, and didn't really trust you. You continued to repeatedly be 'falling out with each other' and having 'slanging matches' and fights, with your 'so called friends'"

"With so many problems at home and school and so few interests, you focused even more on your social life of attracting boys or socialising with them. The 'hanging around' the park or street corners smoking and drinking occurred almost daily and provided many occasions for 'risky or anti-social' behaviour. The 'binge drinking' escalated, as have the anti-social activities they encourage. An example of this, you can see here, is your first contact with illegal drugs, when you had some cannabis, 'a drag on a spliff', as you put it. It gave you the sensation 'to start giggling' that you and your friends thought was 'really cool', which encouraged you to become a regular user."

"However even more significantly, these sessions hanging around with boys, encouraged various sexually related behaviours. Initially this was just a lot of talking about sex, but it soon moved into other areas and I'll use your terms to describe them. First it was 'snogging', then 'fondling and groping', followed by 'hand-jobs', 'fingering' and 'oral sex or blow jobs', with increasing pressure for you to have full sex"

A variety of scenes on the wall illustrated these points, and in each scenario Stacey appeared to be getting older, taller, larger and attempting to look more 'sexy'. The next scene shows Stacey, now about fifteen, dressed in a very low cut top and very short skirt about to enter a night club.

Arthur again commented.

"With such poorly developed motivation skills, boys and sex had now become your only interests and as soon as it was possible, you and your mates started going to night clubs, using false ID, and rapidly you became almost 'addicted' to it. The boys, dancing, loud music, low lights, late nights and binge drinking really appealed to you, instantly becoming your main social activity, but you had very few anyway. Although your parents were very aware of the frequent problems that occur at night clubs, and didn't like you going, you had become very devious at finding ways to go to them, particularly using 'sleepovers at friends houses' as a cover."

"With your desperate desire to attract boys, you went to these clubs 'dressed to attract', which invariably meant wearing very short skirts and displaying your breasts. Your appearance in the clubs does attract a wide variety of boys and men, with most assuming from your appearance that you were much older, much more experienced and very promiscuous. Unfortunately, your poor self awareness, empathy and communication skills sent out messages to girls in the night club that you were trying to steal their boyfriends, so increasingly you became involved in arguments and fights."

Stacey, sitting on her bed, watching these scenes of her life and hearing Arthur's commentary, was becoming increasingly upset. She realised she was observing what she had thought was a very exciting period in her life, but also knew that it would 'turn sour' and cause her huge problems.

Arthur continued.

"The 'pressure' for you to 'lose your virginity' continued to increase, until finally it occurred on a summer evening, in the park, when you were very drunk. Unsurprisingly, it is an experience you struggle to recall very well, and found little pleasure in it. Although he used a condom, you were very worried about whether it had 'slipped off or split' and the possibility of becoming pregnant. You spent many days worrying about this, until your 'period' finally arrived. Despite this first experience of 'sex' being disappointing, your low self esteem due to poor self awareness and motivation skills, meant you felt you had become 'part of the club' among your friends and having sex rapidly became a very common occurrence for you as you felt you had become more attractive to the boys."

"As a result of this promiscuity, two particularly unfortunate events occur for you. One occurs due to you being extremely drunk, as you had unprotected sex with a boy, resulting in you going to the clinic for 'emergency contraception' and discovering you had contracted a sexually transmitted infection, Chlamydia. Your parents now became aware of your 'promiscuity' and yet another huge argument occurred, and you went 'on the pill'. The second event occurred because when you went clubbing, your breasts were always exposed, as you put it 'your boobs hanging out', and you regularly allowed boys to grab them. The pictures of you like this appeared on the internet and you became an object of ridicule, being called slag, slapper, slut, whore etc. You were given the nickname 'booby' which really annoyed you, which resulted in fights, arrest and prosecution for assault".

Stacey was now in tears on her bed, as she watched the scenes of her in the night clubs, she had realised how foolish she had been to make such stupid decisions and how much damage it would do to her in the future.

Chapter 3
Into The Pit Of Despair

The scenes on the wall now showed Stacey yelling at her parents.
Arthur recommenced his commentary.

"Now you are sixteen, your parents feel you should have a 'Weekend Job', to contribute towards the large expenditure you have. However, you have a 'problem with travel and transport', as you think any distance above half a mile is too far to walk, cycling is too embarrassing, and you've never used buses. You regularly used taxis, but expected your parents to 'pick you up and give you lifts' most of the time, using your mobile to call them, using the fact that they were worried about your safety."

"You did manage to get a job, working in a local clothes shop, unfortunately with such poorly developed communication and social skills, you struggled to get on with your manager, workmates and customers, and after only a few weeks you left. A similar situation occurred at school with your two week 'work experience', you felt that it was a waste of time and only reluctantly found a placement in a shop. Again you struggled to get on with your manager, workmates and customers, and left before the end of the two weeks."

The scenes showed Stacey yelling at her manager and workmates.
It then switched to Stacey in school sitting her GCSE exams.
Arthur explained.

"You had given little consideration as to what to do after GCSEs, and with your work experience a disaster and struggling to keep any part-time job, you appeared to have limited options available to interest you after your GCSEs. With such poorly developed learning skills, your poor exam performances continued as you made no real effort to change your approach throughout secondary school. Your GCSE exam results in August were very disappointing and presented you with the problem of what to do next. Your poorly developed cognitive skills meant you decided to do the easiest option, and go to the local college to resit your GCSEs and attempt GNVQs, considering beauty therapy as a possible career."

"Unfortunately, you found studying at college no easier than school, in fact the 'temptation of the new boys' was even more distracting for you. Sadly, your 'booby' nickname and your promiscuous reputation followed you and you continued to have many arguments with other girls, usually about this or about boys or your 'bitchy' comments."

"As you became seventeen, you not only encountered huge problems at college and at home, but your year had several disastrous events, in which a number of deaths to your friends and acquaintances occurred. Your lifestyle had become very careless and risky and you were lucky not have been one of these casualties."

"One of the girls in your tutor class at school was killed when she was hit by a car as she was crossing a road whilst listening to her i-pod, an activity you did many times."

"Another girl in your year at school was killed as a passenger in a full car driven by a boy who had recently passed his test. These accidents occur regularly because the concentration of these young people is usually poor and struggle with the distractions of passengers."

"One of your friends throughout secondary school, Sharon, or 'Shazza' as you called her, died due to a reaction to a tablet she bought that she believed was ecstasy but it was contaminated with other chemicals. With illegal drugs, there is no way of knowing either the strength or the purity of the drug and so taking them is a very high risk activity and these deaths can happen at any time, fortunately it didn't happen to you."

"Adam Firth, the boy with whom you had your first snog, regularly met in the park over the years and had sex with, was killed as the result of a stabbing during a fight outside your favourite night club. Just being around a night club in the early hours of the morning is very risky, you were very lucky to avoid not being caught up in something like that, Adam wasn't."

Stacey was crying profusely on her bed whilst watching scenes of these incidents on the wall, but eventually managed to speak.

"I've always tried to forget about those deaths, I've never thought about it in that way and never considered how lucky I've been, but obviously I have since I've taken lots and lots of risks."

Arthur replied.

"Large numbers of teenagers have such poorly developed cognitive skills that they make so many poor decisions, it becomes 'normal' to them, 'social norms' is the term, and they don't even think about the risks."

"The combination of your inability to cope with college, your huge financial credit card debts, repeated arguments with your parents, and these deaths caused you to become very depressed. Unfortunately, you had no understanding of depression and that most teenagers now experience it, with no idea what you should do. Your pathetic solution was what is often called 'retail therapy and to binge drink', continue to go clubbing and take anti-depressants. To make matters worse, you now became very involved in gambling, spending large sums of money in slot machines and scratch cards."

"Like vast numbers of seventeen and eighteen year olds you couldn't cope with college because you hadn't become an effective independent learner and so left. Fortunately, you did manage to get a job in a shop, because of your mother's influence. She had worked in the local large supermarket, for several years and helped you get a job there. With such low self esteem, you were very reluctant to take it, considering it to be 'beneath you and very embarrassing', but with few alternatives and huge debts you had little choice. Although you began quite well, within a few weeks you started to find the job very difficult for a number of reasons. You considered it boring, and couldn't listen or speak with the customers very well, you 'messed about or chatted up' the young boys on the staff, you weren't very punctual, took days off, and struggled with the 'managers telling you what to do'. You were lucky to survive for a few months, but inevitably you were sacked, and became a 'jobseeker', though that's not really an accurate description, as you did not actually want a job."

"At this time, you were spending quite a lot of time with one of your friends from school, Charlie, who had become a single teenage mother and you helped her to look after her daughter. You actually enjoyed this activity, some of the time anyway, and quite liked the idea of having a home, provided by the council and a baby who needs you. So when you became pregnant, probably because of your inability to remember to regularly take the pill and always use a condom, you were struggling to decide whether to have an abortion or to proceed with it. In the end you decided on abortion because you couldn't bear the thought of giving up smoking, drinking, clubbing, drugs and boys."

"Your life at this time, is still dominated by your focus on 'boys', and of course you have now had numerous sexual partners, many being 'one night stands'. Your poor self awareness and low self esteem means you have a desperate desire to have a 'good reliable boyfriend', but your reputation hinders this possibility because you do not tend to attract those 'sorts of boys'. On many occasions you have felt that you were 'in love' but few have been interested in anything but having sex with you, and so your relationships were short lived. However, you finally 'got your wish' and moved in with a boyfriend who shared a house. Although your parents didn't like your boyfriend, the tension at home was so extreme that your departure was a relief to all."

"You'd only ever lived with your parents and little sister and had struggled with them, but sharing a house with other people, who are not family was even worse, as it is for many. Your poor essential skills meant you found everyone in the house very annoying and continually had arguments with them. Furthermore, apart from sex, you found you had little in common with your boyfriend and after a few months you separated. Fortunately, you'd found another boy who you were able to move in with, who was also sharing a house. Sadly, within a few months exactly the same problem occurs as before, so your boyfriend and the flatmates asked you to leave."

Stacey had watched these scenes from the different houses and commented to Arthur.

"I had no idea that it was so difficult to live with other people, they all seemed so selfish and unpleasant."

Arthur replied immediately.

"Living with people often really tests our essential skills, since they are often stressful environments with little obvious escape. This inability to live with a boyfriend was a bitter blow to you, since throughout your teenage years you had dreamt of living with a boy and when it finally occurred you realised how difficult it was and not the happy situation you'd hoped."

"These problems cause your depression to reach new depths and your parents were very worried about you, so decided to let you to return to their home, with anti-depressants and counselling being prescribed for you. Unfortunately, you were only prepared to take the drugs and refused to have counselling with a psychotherapist, your poor self awareness meant you couldn't cope with having a 'psyche'. You again adopted your usual method of trying to overcome depression; by shopping, drinking and clubbing."

"Predictably, you met a girl in the night club, who got very annoyed when you blatantly flirted with her boyfriend. This girl was very aware of you and your reputation as a 'slut', so you had an argument, and you hit the girl violently, knocking her out. The police were called and with so many witnesses and the assault being recorded on video, you were taken to the police station and charged with 'assault'. Your parents were phoned and collected you from the police station, and brought you back home a few hours ago and here you are now."

"Yes, here we are now." Stacey repeated. "I don't know which is worse, living that life or watching me live it. If I'd gone to the cinema to watch that I don't think I'd believe that a girl could be so stupid. Why did I keep on making so many mistakes, why didn't I learn from any of it, what caused me to be so useless, and as the song says, 'what have I done to deserve this?'"

Arthur responded positively.

"Some interesting questions that can be answered simply by saying, you had not developed the essential skills that you needed to make good decisions. But unfortunately at the moment you do not understand what these essential skills are, how they can be learnt and why you didn't learn them, so my next task is to help you with that, if you want."

"If I want! I don't think I've ever wanted to learn something so much in my life!" Stacey responded very enthusiastically, which was very unusual for her.

Arthur replied immediately.

"In that case, I'd better begin by explaining the essential skills needed to succeed".

Chapter 4
The Skills We Need To Succeed

Stacey adjusted her position on the bed, as if ready for action as the huge slide of the eight essential skills again appeared on the wall.

The skills we need to succeed

Effective Learning
Communication
Cognitive (thinking)
Self-awareness
Managing Feelings
Motivation
Empathy
Social skills

"The first and most essential skill is the 'ability to continually learn effectively'. I pointed out a while ago that humans are born needing to learn to survive, but the situations and difficulties in life in the 21st century are much more complicated than in my day over 50 years ago and continually changing. Unless people continually learn to adapt to these new situations and difficulties they will struggle to cope and many do not. In my day, people could 'get by' in their lives without being able to learn very effectively, because life was so much simpler".

On the wall, scenes of life in the 1950's were shown, men working in factories and women doing housework, to emphasise his point.

"What do you mean, life was so much simpler" Stacey asked.

Arthur answered. "Even in Britain, people worked many hours, had little money, owned few things, had few luxuries, many couldn't read, had few books and televisions were very rare"

"What about the kids, what did they do?" Stacey responded.

"They went to school when they were five and left to go to work when they were 14, most going into manual, simple jobs, except for those who were good at exams, they had more chance of getting well paid careers" Arthur replied.

"But what did the kids do when they weren't at schools?"

"Helping with jobs around the house, playing in the streets and playing games with the family in the house" replied Arthur

"Sounds boring, I'm glad I didn't live in those days" Said Stacey.

"You may think differently in a little while" Arthur responded instantly.

"I doubt it" grunted Stacey.

Arthur continued. "Anyway, the second essential skill is 'Communication'. Humans are not born with a good concentration and attention span, and unless they develop this they will not receive information around them through their senses, see, hear and feel, preventing them from detecting potential problems or danger. Furthermore, humans' ability to convey information at birth is also very limited and unless they can learn to clearly give information to others verbally such as speaking, listening, reading and writing and non-verbally through visual gestures, body language and touch, they struggle to understand each other causing many difficulties"

Suddenly there was a scene on the wall of a baby copying the facial expressions of the mother.

"Well that makes sense, but I don't really understand this non-verbal stuff, what's that all about?" Stacey asked.

Arthur responded. "Humans actually communicate vast quantities of information by the tone of their voice, their facial expressions, like showing fear or confusion, and especially by the shape of their body and positions of their hands, arms and legs, particularly how they touch each other".

Again scenes of people showing different facial expressions, body positions and cuddling each other illustrated Arthur's point.

"Ah yes, I see what you mean". Stacey commented.

"The third essential skill is 'Cognition". Arthur carried on.

"Humans are born struggling to make sense of their world and rely on others to make decisions for them, unless they learn to understand and apply the information they receive they will not be able to recognise difficulties or dangers. For example, working out the connection between the cause of something and the effect it can have, such as realising that a hot or sharp object could cause harm in certain circumstances."

A scene of a young child in a cot gently pulling a blanket to her with a cuddly toy on it gave an example of this.

"This is problem solving, working out why things happen, innit" Stacey asked.

Arthur answered. "Yes, that's basically it, this is one of the skills that is often considered to be especially important in humans. However, in my opinion the most important essential skill to humans is 'Self-awareness'. Humans are unable to understand their emotions and recognize their strengths and weaknesses when they are born, and unless they learn to become aware of them, they are unlikely to respond or behave in a way that overcomes their difficulties. Poor development of self-awareness often results in serious mental health problems and low self-esteem."

"Low self-esteem is something I've heard about, loads of people talk about it, but how do you get self-awareness?" asked Stacey.

"You learn self-awareness; remember it's a skill that can be learnt with lots of actions and reflection" Arthur replied.

"Reflection, what's reflection?" Stacey enquired.

"That's when you think deeply about things" Arthur responded.

"You mean like when you study?" Stacey replied

"Yes, this is a key part of the first essential skill, 'effective learning'. Arthur answered. "This is eventually what happened to Scrooge in 'A Christmas Carol' and George Bailey in 'It's A Wonderful Life', they finally reflected on their lives and became much more self-aware, causing them to change their view of their lives."

"Which is what you are trying to help me do" said Stacey thoughtfully (unusually for her).

"Precisely, the next essential skill is 'Managing Feelings". Arthur continued. "Humans are born unable to manage their emotions or control their impulses. Obviously babies are unable to do this and if humans don't learn to do this, they continue to be controlled by their feelings, preventing them overcoming their difficulties. For example, when toddlers cannot get what they want they get angry, 'losing their temper' often causing harm to either themselves or others. Overcoming difficulties usually relies on 'staying in control', doing what is needed not what is wanted".

Scenes of children and sportsman demonstrating a lack of control (losing their temper) were shown on the wall throughout to illustrate this.

Stacey's face was rigid and went white, as though she'd been inhabited by a ghost, Arthur spotted her expression and commented.

"I've think I've touched a nerve there, perhaps the development of your self-awareness has already begun. In a while you will see how often your poor development of this skill has caused you problems. It also contributes towards the next essential skill 'Motivation'. Humans will experience difficulties from the moment they are born and in the womb; these setbacks help them to learn to become resilient. If children are protected excessively and prevented from experiencing these difficulties, they grow up unprepared to try to overcome difficulties they will meet in the future, which means they will fear failure and avoid challenges or new situations."

Again Stacey's face gave the impression that she'd understood and seen the relevance of this skill to her life, and the scenes of young people injecting and snorting drugs, binge drinking and smoking cigarettes probably helped her make the connection with her own life.

Arthur then resumed. "The seventh essential skill is 'Empathy'. Humans are 'social animals', their success as a species is because they work together as a group and much of their motivation and pleasure involves relationships with others. Unless they learn to become emotionally sensitive to other people and appreciate or 'tune into' their feelings, they falsely believe 'everyone feels the same as they do'. This means they experience many difficulties with other people and frequently have huge relationship problems."

"I've heard of empathy but I didn't know what it meant, I've certainly had a few relationship problems" Stacey commented.

Arthur continued. "I suspect you will also recognise the final one, 'Social skills'. Since relationships are so important to humans, unless they learn to handle a wide variety of relationships and deal effectively with them they are likely to feel lonely, rejected, frustrated, angry and unhappy. The quality of their lives will be greatly affected by how well they 'get on with' other people. Social skills are essential to popularity, effectiveness with others and whether they tend to lead or follow others."

The scenes on the wall showed people arguing, fighting and displaying various sorts of anti-social behaviour.

"Okay, Okay, I get it, these skills, as you call them, are very important, but what's it got to do with me?" Stacey said and was clearly upset.

Arthur responded. "Now that I've explained what the eight essential skills are, I will try to show you how they answer your question 'what have I done to deserve this'. I will try to help you see how different your life would've been if you had learnt these skills much better by the time you began secondary school."

Chapter 5
It's Not A Problem,
It's A Challenge

Stacey's bedroom wall now had a clear picture of Stacey's classroom on her first day at secondary school.

"That's me" exclaimed Stacey. "That's me when I was little" Arthur explained. "Yes, it looks like you but the only difference with you at that age is inside her head, she has learnt the eight essential skills well, so thinks and feels differently to you when she starts secondary school. This Stacey has been looking forward to her first day at secondary school for a long time. Although this a very new experience for her, she thinks of it as a challenge, an adventure, not filled with the dread that you did. She actually feels quite confident because at least a dozen children from her class in primary school are also starting there at same time and is looking forward to meeting them again. Also she liked Mr Brown, her tutor, when they met last term, as he reminded her of Clark Kent."

"Why does she think like that, I dreaded that day" Stacey asked.

Arthur answered. "This is because this Stacey, I'll call her 'Skilful Stacey', has developed her motivation skills and has learnt to view difficulties as challenges that will help her to succeed. Her attitude is the greater the difficulty the greater the feeling of success when it has been overcome."

As Arthur said this a huge slide poster appeared on the wall.

Success = Overcoming Difficulties

This gradually faded and replaced by another one.

The Greater The Difficulty
The Greater The Success

The posters faded away and a scene of Stacey in her classroom resumed. Young Stacey was sat down next to Lucy, who immediately introduced herself.

"Pleased to meet you, I'm Stacey, which school did you go to?"

They started chatting away and soon got to know each other and realised they had quite a few interests in common. The next instant, it was lunchtime, and they both went off to have their packed lunches together, continuing their chatting in the dining hall.

The next scene showed young Stacey and Lucy with some of her old friends that she'd persuaded to take a slightly longer route home to go via Lucy's house, they were all chatting and laughing about their day.

These scenes caused Stacey to be amazed at how different this young Stacey was to her at that age and she asked.

"How did she make friends so easily with Lucy, what did she have to talk about all the time and why is she so happy?"

Arthur immediately replied.

"She'd learnt to empathise with people; she's learnt to ask good probing questions and listens very carefully to their answers. Gradually she has learnt good communication and social skills, so enjoys meeting new people and develop new friendships"

The scene on the wall then shows young Stacey arriving home from her first day at school, she couldn't wait to tell her mum all about her day. She talked for ages, and repeated it all when her dad came home. Her mum and dad both ended up recounting their memories of their first day at secondary school and how 'exhausting and confusing' they found it, helping Stacey to feel even better.

Stacey commented on these scenes.

"This 'Skilful Stacey' is so excited; I hated the first day and wanted to forget all about it."

Arthur then explained.

"Because this Stacey has developed her communication and social skills she enjoys sharing her experiences with others, especially her family, because your skills were lacking you struggled to do this and reluctant to talk to your family about school, especially when things were difficult. Skilful Stacey, also struggled in her first weeks but discussed her difficulties with her family who helped her overcome them."

The scenes on the wall now showed young Stacey with a frustrated and concerned expression sitting around the dining table talking to her parents. The conversation illustrated that her difficulties with doing homework and getting organised each day was worrying her. Her mother said she used to find using a diary helped her 'keep on top of things' and her father suggested she tries to keep to a time limit on her homework rather than just doing it until she thinks she's finished, agreeing to spend a maximum of 2 hours on homework, and inform her tutor of any particular difficulties.

"I wish my parents had been that helpful" Stacey commented.

Arthur promptly replied.

"You never gave them a chance, you wouldn't sit and discuss your problems with them, and you tended to either shout at them or just keep very quiet, you hadn't developed your communication and social skills enough to discuss your difficulties with them"

Stacey's expression showed she'd realised that this was very true.

The scenes on the wall now depicted young Stacey in school and showing her finding it difficult to concentrate and understand her 8 different teachers in some of the lessons. She is discussing these difficulties with her classmates, who have a similar problems, and they make a pact to become the 'non-silent minority', discussing their difficulties with each other and their tutor.

"Skilful Stacey is so lucky, I wish I'd had friends like that" remarked Stacey.

Arthur immediately responded.

"Luck was not the reason, you could've had them as friends but you rejected them in favour of ones who were superficial and lazy. Your poor communication and social skills meant you only had relationships with people who were similar to you, more concerned with superficial things, appearances, boys and 'having a laugh', as you called it. It takes empathy, time and effort to develop good quality relationships like these, and you were unable to do this".

Again Stacey's expression showed that she had realised that Arthur had spoken the truth.

There were now pictures of young Stacey taking part in various after-school clubs and activities, such as sport, music, drama and dance, and it shows her talking to her friends expressing to them that although she feels she has limited abilities in them, she thinks it's worth 'giving it a go and it'll be a laugh'.

Stacey was confused at what she'd seen and heard and asked.

"Why is this 'Skilful Stacey' taking part in these activities, but I wouldn't?"

Arthur replied.

"Self-esteem is the estimation that we have of ourselves that depends on our values and capabilities. Your poorly developed self-awareness meant that you had little real idea of your capabilities and your poor social skills meant you were easily lead by others. Your values were largely determined by other people and the media, television and magazines etc. Your low self-esteem explains why when you felt you were no good at sport, music, drama or dance, you were too frightened to try because you would be 'shown up and laughed at'. Although 'Skilful Stacey' also feels she may have limited abilities in sport, music, drama and dance', her good self-motivation and social skills prevent this being used as an excuse not to try new experiences and challenges or pass up a chance to learn new skills.

Now look what has happened to young Stacey after only a few weeks at these clubs and activities"

The scenes on the wall showed Stacey showing pleasure and clear progress in all of these activities and being selected for the school netball and hockey teams, as well as the school choir and a part in the school play.

Stacey was again confused and asked.

"How has she become so good, I never had that talent"

Arthur responded.

"We are not born able to do these things we learn how to do them, and improve with practice. You would've achieved all of this if you had been prepared to try and practise, but your poor development in the skills of effective learning and motivation, meant you didn't try or practise. The selection of 'Skilful Stacey' for the netball, hockey, choir and school play surprised her parents as they had not previously thought she was particularly 'talented' but continually encouraged her."

The scenes on the wall now showed young Stacey on her way home being offered a cigarette by one of the girls in her class (not a usual friend) and proceeding to have a big argument with her. It almost ends in blows, with young Stacey explaining it contributed to her grandfather's death. She could be heard clearly and loudly asking 'give me one good reason to start smoking'. The silence and expression on the girls' face completely deflated her and she said.

" Exactly, there are none" and stormed off.

Stacey responded on watching this.

"I wish I hadn't started smoking, why didn't I do that?"

Arthur then answered.

"There appear to be no good reasons to start smoking, but almost everybody starts smoking because their skill at managing their feelings is poorly developed. Basically they know that they should not start smoking but their emotions control their actions and they do."

The next scene showed young Stacey's parents receiving a letter from the school to congratulate Stacey on her 'Excellent Attitude and Progress'. Although Stacey had been a reasonable pupil at primary school, this had not occurred before, and so she and her parents are greatly surprised and proud of her success in her first year at secondary school. However, the next scenes show Stacey getting disappointing exam marks and then discussing it with her parents around the dining table. Young Stacey clearly put in a lot of effort to revise for her exams, and her parents point out that they had similar difficulties when they were children. This was followed by a discussion with her tutor in which Stacey realised that she did not prepare for her exams very effectively, despite spending a lot of time on it.

"I was rubbish at exams as well" remarked Stacey, forgetting that the scenes were showing the difficulties she actually had.

Arthur instantly responded.

"But what did you do about? 'Skilful Stacey's good development of self-awareness and motivation meant that she wanted to find our why she had not been successful and how she could overcome the difficulties, you just looked for excuses"

Stacey's face again showed she'd realised it was true.

The scenes on the wall now showed young Stacey during the summer break playing sports, attempting drama and dance activities, and performing in a 'not very good' musical group, all with her friends.

Arthur commented.

"Because Skilful Stacey has well developed Motivation and Social skills, she finds pleasure in a huge range of activities and is therefore rarely bored."

Chapter 6
Short Term Pain, Long Term Gain

The next scene on the wall of Stacey's bedroom shows young Stacey in her bedroom propped up on her bed reading.

The layout of the bedroom prompted Stacey to remark whilst pointing at her huge TV screen high up on the wall and the computer to her left.

"Where's the television and computer? There should be a large TV in that corner and the computer over there"

Arthur replied straightaway.

"Skilful Stacey doesn't have them in her bedroom, she and her parents decided that it was not a good idea, as they're too distracting and anti-social. All the televisions and computers are shared by the whole family and kept downstairs so that they can all easily use them. This is an excellent example of Stacey's good cognitive and managing feelings skills. Although she would like them in her bedroom, she understands the problems they are likely to cause in the long term, and makes the decision to not have them in her bedroom. This has meant that when Stacey is studying she can be helped or encouraged. She often watches TV and videos with her family, and they use it as a focus for discussion and sharing interests. Furthermore, Skilful Stacey has now become an avid reader of fiction books, which helps develop her effective learning and empathy skills."

Stacey commented on what Arthur had said.

"This Stacey is nothing like me"

Arthur continued.

"You're right; she does become less and less like you, as we go on. You're beginning to see that these essential skills, determine so much of our lives and this is a clear reflection of this, but you ain't seen nothing' yet. This next scene will demonstrate another major difference"

The scenes on the wall show young Stacey and her friends being criticised and 'bitched about' by other girls. The sound increases so that the discussions between her friends can be clearly heard; they are discussing why this might be occurring and how important it is to continue to support each other,

Arthur explains.

"Skilful Stacey's good cognitive and empathy skills, means she understands and even expects some girls with low self-esteem to be jealous of her and her friends, and her good development of managing feelings keeps her in control despite the antagonism."

The pictures of Stacey show her having a number of discussions with her parents.

Arthur adds. "Skilful Stacey has really got to know them quite well, their difficulties in childhood, their values, their emotions and they have got to know her very well, and they've developed a great deal of trust and respect between them."

Stacey commented on this observation.

"I just couldn't talk to my parents; we always ended up just shouting at each other, they never understood me at all"

Arthur then replied.

"Respect for each other, means you care and consider each others' views and feelings, it takes a long time to develop through a great deal of openness, honesty and fairness. There was very little of this in your life, and your poor development of the essential skills meant you were incapable of displaying the level of openness, honesty and fairness necessary to achieve this sort of relationship and respect".

Stacey looked very glum, knowing that Arthur was right once again.

The next scenes showed young Stacey doing exercises in her bedroom, keeping a record of her food calorie input and weight, eating healthy foods and buying some clothes.

Stacey commented on this scene.

"I wouldn't be seen dead in those clothes, I don't even recognise the labels, and why is she doing all this exercise and measuring calories?"

Arthur answered.

"As you are aware you've struggled with your weight for a number of years and been very concerned about your appearance, but this Stacey has developed good self-awareness and cognitive skills, so understands that regular exercise and healthy eating is the way to control it. Because your skills were so poor you either ate nothing or the wrong things and then binged, exercise was too much effort for you. Furthermore, because your self-awareness was so poorly developed, your low self-esteem caused you to spent a fortune on your appearance, especially buying clothes with expensive labels, in the hope that others would be impressed"

"But everyone does that" Stacey attempted to defend herself.

Arthur replied.

"No they don't, but it appeared like that to you, since the people you were friends with and the people you admired did so, remember it's called 'social norms', we get a very distorted picture of what is normal because of our limited contacts and information".

On the wall, the scenes showed young Stacey now doing housework and delivering newspapers.

"What's this all about?" Stacey quizzed.

Arthur responded.

"She's trying to earn money, and following discussions with her parents, young Stacey has attempted to calculate how much it costs to live at home and here's what they came up with."

Arthur continued.

Stacey's weekly expenses if she didn't live at home

Rent	**£50**
Council Tax	**£10**
Water Rates	**£10**
Electricity	**£7**
Gas	**£8**
Food	**£35**
Total	**£120**

NOT including mobile phone, clothes, social activities or travel expenses

---

"This calculation shook young Stacey and she felt she should try to contribute in some way. So she offered to do 'the same as her mother did' in 'doing jobs around the house' and also gets a part time job, 'as her father did', delivering local papers."

On hearing and seeing this, Stacey responded in an unusually mature tone. "I had no idea it cost so much to live, until I left home. If you add on the weekly cost of the mobile phone, clothes, travel and social life, it would be double that amount".

Suddenly the wall lights up in yellow with this poster.

SUPERlearning
For Exam Success

S	**S**TART WITH THE END IN MIND – you must START by attempting past exam papers, marking them and then using the EXAM ANALYSIS to ensure you are ONLY focusing on YOUR key difficulties
U	**U**NDERSTAND YOUR LEARNING –you must be sure you are clear on YOUR difficulties and how YOU can overcome them.
P	**P**ERSONALISE YOUR LEARNING – you need to apply YOUR most effective styles and techniques for learning (eg videostudy etc)
E	**E**VALUATE YOUR LEARNING – you must keep TESTING YOURSELF to keep checking that you are making progress, so you avoid wasting YOUR efforts and don't give up!
R	**R**ESOURCES FOR YOUR EFFECTIVE LEARNING – you only use the resources that focus on YOUR exam papers and difficulties, using YOUR most effective styles and techniques for learning
l e a r n i n g	

Arthur explained.

"Stacey's well developed self-motivation meant that she was determined to learn from her poor exam performance in her first year and discovered a new approach. She learnt to view tests and exams like matches in sport, and prepares for them by focusing on the key parts needed to succeed (she calls it SUPERlearning). Her exam performance improved enormously, and she shared the techniques with her friends (and anyone who asks her). The feeling she experienced from the success of this approach was huge as she had used such a wide range of skills to create it, and it was extremely effective, From this moment Stacey would not only start to improve rapidly at exams, she had developed an effective approach to learning for the rest of her life"

Stacey was again amazed and commented.

"That's what I needed, a way of being good at exams"

Arthur instantly responded

"No its not just an effective approach for success in exams, its an effective approach for success in anything".

The next scene shows Stacey and her parents at a school parent's consultation evening.

Arthur gives a commentary

"Skilful Stacey's parents are shocked and extremely proud of the incredible improvement that she has made, largely due to her SUPERlearning approach. They have learnt a lot from Stacey and have become aware of how they can support her at home by showing an interest in her studies and asking her to explain it to them."

Chapter 7
'Success in life is a marathon not a sprint'

The scenes on the wall show Stacey drinking alcohol in a house with her friends. Arthur quickly commented

"This Skilful Stacey will 'binge drink' alcohol but unlike you, very occasionally and is very cautious, avoiding too much 'loss of control', and ensuring she is supported by her friends. Her very good cognitive skills means she understands the effects of alcohol and uses it very effectively"

"What do you mean 'she uses it very effectively'?" asks Stacey.

Arthur explains.

"The front part of the human brain manages emotions and prevent the emotions taking over. Alcohol tends to reduce this controlling effect of this front part of the brain, so gradually humans behave in a way that their emotions determine. If they are angry or frustrated, the alcohol means they tend to become aggressive, if they are feeling low or depressed the alcohol can cause them to feel very sorrow for themselves or suicidal"

Stacey felt the need to comment.

"I usually became more sociable when I had a drink"

Arthur responded to this comment.

"That's because your poorly developed self-awareness and social skills meant you had low self-esteem and although you desperately wanted people to like you, especially boys, you struggled to achieve this, but your emotions took over when alcohol hit your brain and you said or did anything to try to attract them. Unfortunately the people you were trying to attract or impress had little respect for you, and merely used you for their own gain."

Again Stacey looked really upset, realising Arthur was explaining the situation very accurately.

A scene of Stacey with her friends in a night club now appeared on the wall, with her in a fairly low cut top and fairly short skirt, being 'chatted up' by a boy.

"I recognise that place, I must've been in that club over a hundred times and picked up by hundreds of boys" Stacey stopped abruptly, as she realised she was expressing the problems that Arthur had just been describing.

Arthur continued.

"Yes, I'm afraid your low self-esteem meant you invariably went out, caked in make-up and wearing extremely low cut tops to show off what you thought was your only positive asset. Unfortunately, both the boys and girls interpreted from this that you were 'desperate', and prepared to have sex with any boy, which you usually did. Your poorly developed social skills meant unless they were having sex with you, they weren't really interested in you. What made things worse for you was your poor communication skills meant you didn't detect the facial expressions, voice intonations and body language of the girls and got into a number of arguments and fights as a result."

As Stacey was listening to this, tears were forming in her eyes, as she realised that Arthur's explanation was perfectly correct, and understood why she could never get a 'good relationship' and had numerous fights.

Arthur continued.

"Because this Skilful Stacey has such well developed skills, she is able to communicate and socialise with a wide range of people, and boys are attracted to her because she is so interesting. Her body language and appearance communicates that she is confident, making her even more attractive."

Stacey is prompted to ask.

"What about taking drugs? This Skilful Stacey drinks alcohol, goes clubbing and attracts boys, does she take drugs?" Arthur responds. "Remember this is you, or more to the point this is the life you would've had if you'd learnt the essential skills, you would still have drunk alcohol and gone clubbing but in a more moderate and controlled manner. The boys would've been much more attracted to you if you had not been so 'desperate' due to your poor skill development. You would not have taken illegal drugs if you had good cognitive skills and learnt to manage your feelings because you would've understood the high risk of taking illegal drugs. These high risk activities are often perceived as a 'rite of passage' or 'code of behaviour' to belong to a group and taking illegal drugs is an excellent example of this, as the effects are very uncertain as there is no guarantee of it's purity or the concentration. Unlike you, this Stacey has no reason to consider doing such a stupid activity."

The scenes of Stacey in the night club faded and replaced by her serving in a clothes shop.

"I recognise this place as well, this is the shop I had my work experience in." Stacey commented.

Arthur then comments.

"But you only lasted a few days, because of your lack of essential skills. Virtually all employers want 'the ability to work in teams' from their employees above anything else, and because you hadn't learnt the skills needed to achieve this you struggled in all your jobs. This Skilful Stacey has learnt good communication and social skills and also has a good development of managing emotions, so she is considered to be an excellent employee."

The scene on the wall showed Stacey playing a number of sports and being the captain of successful netball and hockey teams, winning trophies, followed by her being in school drama and musical productions.

"How did I come to be so good a sports and stuff?" Stacey commented realising that she was now actually watching an alternative version of herself.

Arthur replies.

"Although at the age of 11 you may have considered you had limited ability, like most children you had huge potential which with a 'growth mindset' would've brought huge improvement. Unfortunately your poorly developed motivation meant you feared failure and avoided difficulties and so did not improve. This Skilful Stacey has a simple but effective approach"

Arthur raised his arm and pointed at the huge poster on the wall.

Success in life is a marathon not a sprint.

It requires short term pain to achieve long term gain

Arthur continued

"Successful people use their difficulties to improve by learning from the experience and setbacks; sometimes they are described as having a growth mindset, so she's become very talented in various areas"

"So you're telling me that I could've done all that" Stacey asked.

"You've forgotten, this is you, with the 8 essential skills. You also would've achieved a great deal of exam success"

A scene showing Stacey taking her GCSE exams and receiving an excellent set of grades was then shown on the wall.

Arthur explained.

"Stacey's skills helped her create her 'SUPERlearning' which meant she overcame her previous poor exam performances and she achieved excellent GCSE exam results and studied A levels at the local college."

A scene on the wall showed a young girl shouting at a baby, then drinking from a bottle of vodka, and taking anti-depressants.

Stacey recognised this scene and commented.

"That's Charlie, she so wanted a baby but when he was born she just couldn't cope. I envied her at the start, 'cos she seemed so happy and everyone flocked around her but her baby needed so much attention, Charlie couldn't do anything and got so depressed, I quickly changed my mind and thought I was glad it wasn't me".

Arthur responded.

"Yes, a rare occasion, where you actually learnt from someone else's experience, but you certainly had numerous sexually related problems to learn from. Your numerous 'one night stands', contributed towards your abortion, several 'emergency contraception' occasions and two bouts of sexually transmitted infections.

Arthur again pointed to the wall, where pictures illustrated his points.

"If you had developed your management of emotions, cognitive and social skills you would've avoided all of that by having a life that is very busy and enjoyable. Your time spent trying to juggle college life, studies, work, friends, sporting activities, appearing in plays and musicals, as well having a few boyfriends, some as sexual partners, Applying these skills in discussions and reflections with friends, boyfriends and family would've helped you learnt a lot about love, liking and lust, as this poster illustrates.

(SEE NEXT PAGE)

Stacey read the poster and a huge lump appeared in her throat, she struggled to hold back the tears but managed to comment.

"If only I had realised that, I never seemed to have good relationships with my family, friends or boyfriends".

Arthur explained.

Stacey's Understanding of Love, Like and Lust

Love

- I feel I can be completely open and honest with them (I trust them completely).
- I would do almost anything for them. Their welfare is one of my main concerns.
- I feel much better when I am with them.

Like

- I admire their qualities and skills.
- I get on well with them.

Lust

- I desire them a great deal. I'd like to have sex with them.

"Sadly too few people at present really understand what is needed to develop good relationships despite it being one of their greatest desires. Developing empathy through a great deal of quality discussion and reflection is too rare for most people to achieve excellent relationships, and having sex so quickly seems to add to their confusion, it is such a shame. Look how popular Skilful Stacey is at university, and despite having to live with a very wide range of people, she manages to get on with almost everybody because her social and other essential skills are so well developed"

The scenes on the wall demonstrate Stacey enjoying university life. Stacey is clearly shocked and asks.

"You mean I could've gone to university, I don't believe it"

Arthur calmly replies.

"Of course you could, if only you had developed effective learning skills, but unfortunately, a lot of students don't develop all the essential skills enough to allow them to cope living away from home and drop out of university. Throughout her teenage years Skilful Stacey had had several friends diagnosed with depression and then become aware that depression and self harm is not uncommon in universities, with several of her fellow students taking anti-depressants and having counselling. In fact, she'd been so impressed by the effectiveness of counselling that she'd trained as a counsellor and used her essential skills to help others who are struggling to cope."

Again Stacey's mouth was open in amazement, but managed a comment.

"So instead of suffering from depression, committing self harm and attempting suicide, I could've been helping to prevent others doing just that"

"If you'd learnt the essential skills, yes." Replied Arthur.

Chapter 8
It's never too late to learn to succeed

"OK you've answered the question – 'What have I done to deserve this', I did not develop the skills I needed to succeed! But why have you shown me all this? Why are you here? What is the point of all this?"

Stacey's comment reflected the confusion etched all over her face. Arthur replied.

"I wondered when you'd ask that, you've listened and observed all this much better than I thought you would. Clearly you can learn if you put your mind to it, that's encouraging."

"Why is it encouraging? Please explain this to me." Stacey pleaded.

"And you said 'please', that's very unusual for you" Arthur commented.

Stacey's face now looked quite pitiful as was her tone.

Arthur continued.

"When I first appeared we decided to consider me as a ghost or angel like the ones that appeared in 'It's a Wonderful Life' and 'A Christmas Carol', and like them I would try to develop your self-awareness. I think I have achieved that, you now seem to be aware that your life could've been successful if you'd learnt the essential skills needed to succeed."

Stacey regained some of her composure and replied.

"Yes, I do realise that now, but what use is it?"

Arthur responded.

"In both those stories, George and Scrooge were sort of given another chance."

"Am I going to get another chance?" Stacey asked.

"If you did, what would you do with it?" Arthur asked.

"Whatever you suggest" Stacey answered instantly.

"OK, well here's my suggestion". Arthur said. "You are never too old to learn, but learning gets more difficult with increasing age and if you are willing, you could still develop the skills you need to succeed."

Stacey was clearly surprised and excited and asked.

"Do you really think I could? I've not been very good at learning so far."

Arthur replied.

"But it could be different for you in the future because you will be aware of the five learning requirements and SUPERlearning."

Stacey then responded.

"SUPERlearning you've shown me, but what are the five learning requirements?"

Arthur pointed at the wall and said.

"There they are!"

THE FIVE LEARNING REQUIREMENTS
Whatever you are trying to learn you need the following:

MOTIVATION	*Unless we are keen to learn, we will lack the determination to overcome the difficulties that will occur.*
CONCENTRATION	*If we do not focus on the task, our brain cannot receive or store the information needed.*
ENVIRONMENT	*Distractions can cause concentration to become too difficult to allow us to learn,*
ATTAINABLE TASKS	*Unless the task to be learnt is broken down into small steps ('bitesize chunks') they are too difficult to grasp ('too large to digest').*
FEELING SUCCESS	*If we do not feel we are making progress it becomes too difficult to keep motivated.*

Stacey carefully studied the poster, and said.

"How will I be able to remember all this information."

"I will help you" replied Arthur.

"How" she asked.

"As I am now, whenever you really need me, I will try to prompt you" Arthur responded.

"Why haven't you appeared before?" She questioned.

"You didn't need me enough, your motivation to learn has not been great enough until now, this is your 'now or never' moment, the 'point of no return' He answered.

"So what exactly do I have to do, I'll do anything to finally live a decent life" Stacey pleaded.

"From now on you must do all that you can to learn the skills you need to succeed and help others do the same"

"You want me to help others learn these skills as well! How can I do that if I don't have them myself" Stacey said struggling to believe it.

"Because in order for you to learn them, you will need to understand how and this will help you to help others to do the same". Arthur replied.

Stacey's face radiated for the first time in years, she struggled to recall the last time someone showed confidence in her, and the feeling was strange but wonderful.

"But I have no idea how to learn these skills" She asked.

Arthur responded.

"Now that you're finally motivated to learn, we'll focus on how these skills can be learnt, but that will occur when your concentration and the environment is suitable. It is time for me to leave now and allow this learning to be put into practice."

"You're leaving? So what happens now?"

"Well that's up to you" Arthur replied. "I will return when you are ready"

"When will that be, when will I be ready for another visit?" Stacey asked.

"I will decide that" Arthur promptly replied." But it will be soon."

With that he held his hand high as to wave goodbye, and a bright light grew behind him until his shape became just a black outline. Stacey 'was almost 'blinded by the light', and scrunched her eyes shut very tightly to protect them. When she tried to open them again there was still a bright light with a black shape in front of it, but the shape had changed, it looked more like a head just in front of her. She could hear a different voice, it wasn't Arthur, it sounded like a female's voice, and in fact it sounded like her mother's.

"She's waking up, her eyes are opening" It was her mother's voice.

"Stace, Stace, are you OK, it's me, it's your mum".

Stacey's eyes were now completely open and focused, it was her mother's face she could see, Stacey looked around and saw her father,

"Mum, dad, where am I? What's happened?" Stacey finally managed to splutter.

"Stace, you're in hospital, you passed out and you were sick, we didn't know what you'd done, so we phoned for an ambulance" Her mother explained.

Stacey could now see there was a nurse in the room, who bent over Stacey and examined her eyes and took her pulse.

"Mmm, she seems OK, She said. I'll get the doctor to have a look at her"

The nurse left the room, Stacey looked around and could see just one other bed in it, but that was empty.

"You drank almost a whole bottle of vodka, took some paracetamol and passed out. I think we came into your room just after you passed out and we called an ambulance. Stacey's father explained. "How are you feeling?"

"I've got a shocking headache" Stacey replied.

Stacey was now able to remember what had happened, and recalled the vodka and the paracetamol, but more importantly she was able to remember Arthur and vividly recalled her time with him.

"How long have I been asleep" Stacey asked.

"Two or three hours, we were so worried, we should've realised how upset you were and that you would do something stupid, but we were so angry." Stacey's mother replied and hugged her.

"I shouldn't have shouted at you Stace, but.." Stacey's father struggled to say anymore and was clearly struggling to speak.

"No dad, mum, it's me, I shouldn't have treated you in this way, I'm so sorry, please forgive me." Stacey said with her eyes full of tears.

"I've been so stupid and selfish, I've caused you so much grief, can you ever forgive me?" she added.

Stacey's parents were speechless; neither could recall Stacey showing such remorse.

"I realise how unfair I've been and I'm going to change, I promise". Stacey added.

"What's brought this about, why now, you've never spoken like this before" said a shocked Stacey's mother.

"Your granddad, mum, Arthur. He's shown me what I've done to deserve this and what I must learn in order to change" Stacey replied.

Stacey's mother looked absolutely astonished and said.

"My granddad Arthur? You've never met him, he was dead years before you were born, what's he got to do with it?"

Stacey responded.

"He may be dead, but I've still met him, he's been with me for hours and has already taught me loads"

"Clearly the vodka and paracetamol have caused you some very interesting hallucinations" Stacey's father commented.

"Possibly, I don't think so, but whatever it was, I'm not going to waste the chance to learn and change" Stacey immediately replied.

"I don't understand what you're going on about, or why you should bring Arthur into it, but I just hope you do change, we can't go through this again. Stacey's mother although bewildered managed to respond.

"I will mum, I promise. Will you help me change; will you help me learn to succeed?" Stacey pleaded.

Stacey's father grabbed her hand with both his and said.

"If you really mean it, if you are really going to try this time, we will help you, but we can't cope with another night like this one."

"Don't worry dad, I wont, you're going to see a skilful successful Stacey from now on" Stacey answered.

Stacey's mother and father looked at each other in amazement, struggling to understand what Stacey was saying and believe what they were hearing, but they just desperately wanted it to be true.

Chapter 9
'Let The Learning Begin'

When Stacey woke up in her bedroom the following day, although she still had a slight headache, she got up with a positive attitude that she'd probably never had before. She began by deciding to not smoke another cigarette, tidying up her bedroom and redesigning it as a study room. It would be a great understatement to say that Stacey's parents and sister were surprised, summed up by her father's 'joke'.

"So who's stolen my daughter and replaced her with this Stepford Child?"

Suzi, Stacey's younger sister was particularly confused and plonked herself down on Stacey's bed and began asking questions.

"So what's happening Sis, what you doing?"

"I'm starting my new life, Suze. I've been given a second chance and I ain't gonna waste it." Stacey replied.

"What do you mean 'given a second chance'?"

Stacey explained.

"Two nights ago, I was so fed up with my life that I tried to commit suicide, I downed a bottle of vodka and loads of pills and passed out. But while I was asleep or something, mum's granddad, 'Arthur' appeared in this room in front of me and showed me why I messed up my life and what it could've been like. You know, like in the film 'It's a Wonderful Life', and convinced me that I could 'turn myself around' and become a success."

Suzi was obviously confused and asked.

"What do you mean, you had a dream with mum's grandad talking to you?"

Stacey tried to respond.

"Well, It seemed too real to be a dream, and I can remember all of it so well, I don't think it was. But I don't know how to explain it"

"So what happened in this dream or whatever?" Suzi asked and was clearly fascinated.

"This wall became a giant video screen and I saw loads of my life from about your age, and then someone who wasn't actually me, she looked like me but behaved differently. The same things tended to happen to her, but she handled them completely differently, much better, and she became a really talented successful girl, the complete opposite of me, in fact."

Suzi was both confused and astonished but managed to say.

"Wow, but what was different about her, why did she become a success and you didn't?"

Stacey continued to try to explain.

"That was precisely the point Arthur was making. This 'Skilful Stacey' had learnt 8 essential skills by your age, much better than I did, so kept making good decisions instead of the stupid ones that I did."

Suzi was now further confused, asked.

"What 8 essential skills?"

"I can't really remember them, precisely. The first was definitely 'Effective Learning', another was 'Communication', 'Self-Awareness and Motivation were two others, I'm struggling with the rest"

Despite being very confused, Suzi was so pleased with her 'new sister' she remained focused and asked.

"So how you going to 'turn your life around' if you can't even remember what these skills are?"

Despite struggling to explain clearly, Stacey remained enthusiastic and added.

"Arthur said he would help me, he said he would keep prompting me, so I'm preparing the walls for posters and the room for study."

"So he's going to come back?" Suzi asked.

"I believe, so" Stacey replied with look of uncertainty etched all over her face.

"That's a brilliant story, Sis, it's like 'Narnia' or 'Harry Potter'" Suzi said in an enthusiastic tone.

"Or Christmas Carol." Stacey added. "I'm going to start reading that today, I've always liked that film"

"Is that the one with Scrooge in it?" Suzi asked.

"Yeah that's it" Stacey replied.

Suzi quickly responded. "I think it's on TV over Christmas, if it is, perhaps we can watch it together.

"A great idea, Suze" Stacey replied, also enthusiastic

When do you think you'll get to see Arthur again?" Suzi asked.

"I don't know, but I hope it's soon" Stacey responded.

"When he does, will you let me know" Suzi said excitedly.

"Of course, I will. In fact Arthur said he wants me to do all that I can to help others learn these skills as well, and I reckon he probably wants me to start with you" Stacey commented.

"Oh I do hope so, it's so much nicer having a sister who actually listens and talks to me, instead of ignoring or just shouting at me" Suzi said with real emotion in her tone.

Stacey's face went pale, she realised with that comment how horrible a sister she'd been for so many years, most of Suzi's life in fact. She got on the bed with Suzi and hugged her tightly, and with her eyes beginning to stream with tears she said.

"I'm so sorry, Suze, your right, how horrible I've been, I'm so sorry, please forgive me, I'll try to make it up to you, I promise. I won't be that Stacey again, she's gone for good."

Suzi felt so happy, she began crying, she'd always wanted and wished for a nice, loving sister and that's the first time she could recall ever feeling she might actually have one!

Both Suzi and Stacey went to bed that night reflecting on a momentous day, each feeling they'd just discovered a new sister.

"Well I am impressed, you've started very well"

Stacey awoke suddenly as a result of this voice.

"Arthur, you've come back!" She said in a surprised tone.

"Of course, I have, did you doubt me?" Arthur replied.

"No, not really, it's just that recounting your visit seemed to make it more difficult to believe." She answered.

"I think you've handled that very well, you seem to have accepted my visit and message comfortably, and your interaction with your sister today was wonderful" Arthur responded.

"I already feel better, merely because I'm trying to be positive" Arthur then explained.

"You are already displaying a 'Growth Mindset', so crucial to learning and success. My visits from now on will be much shorter and more focused to ensure you have a chance to put each part into action."

"That's good, 'cos there was so much to take in the other night". Stacey commented.

Arthur then answered.

"I realise that, but it was necessary to convince you of the need to change, the task is now to help you with this learning. I suggest you keep a pad and pen next to your bed to note down key points as soon as you can and help you recall them. Your first task is to learn what the 8 essential skills are that we need to succeed and begin to assess yourself and others in them"

"How do I do that?" Stacey asked.

"Just search the internet for 'Skills We Need To Succeed'. I also want you to watch 'Child Of Our Time' from the start and observe how these skills are being developed in the children." Arthur suggested

"What's 'Child Of Our Time'?" Stacey looked very confused.

"It's a BBC TV series that began in the year 2000, annually studying the lives of about 25 children born at that time, and you can view them on BBC i-player."

"Is that it?" Stacey enquired.

"Yes, that's all for this time, I'll see you again soon, keep up the good work." Arthur answered and as before, he departed by raising his arm and disappearing as the light behind him grew brighter.

Stacey woke up, unsure of whether Arthur had just left or it happened hours ago, but she immediately got up and searched for a pen and paper. Stacey excitedly wrote down on the pad she found;

'Skills we need to succeed'

'Child of our time'

She then went to Suzi's room, and tapped on the door

"Are you awake?" she asked quietly

"Yeah, come in Sis" Suzi replied.

"He came, Arthur visited me again" Stacey said as she sat on the side of Suzi's bed.

"What did he say?" Suzi asked

"Not much this time, only he wants me to learn about the 'Skills we need to succeed' and watch a programme called 'Child of our time', have you ever come across it?"

"I've heard of it, but never seen it. What's it about?" Suzi asked.

"It's a series that's on BBC every year showing about 20 kids growing up, apparently it's been going on for about 8 years" Stacey explained.

"Sounds interesting, perhaps we can watch it together" Suzi asked hopefully

"Yeah, of course we can, Arthur wants me to help others learn anyway. I've got to find out about these essential skills first, though. So I'm going to have a shower, have some breakfast and then go on the internet on my computer, do you want to help? Stacey asked.

"Oh yes please" Suzi replied excitedly

See you in a little while, then" Stacey said as she got up and left the room.

Suzi sat up in her bed and clenched her fists as if she'd just scored a goal in football, she was so pleased to have sister to be with, a 'tear in her eye and a lump in her throat' illustrated her delight.

Stacey and Suzi spent the morning on the computer downloading and printing articles, they then created 2 posters that summarised the key points of the 8 essential skills needed to succeed and stuck it on Stacey's bedroom wall.

The 8 Skills We Need To Succeed

Effective Learning Skills

We need to learn to survive but unless we develop our ability to learn throughout our life the continually changing situations and difficulties in the 21st century will destroy/ defeat us.

Communication skills

We are not born with a good concentration or able to understand and convey information, unless we learn to communicate effectively, we cannot form good relationships by sharing our emotions. It is also needed to learn effectively, requiring good development of our Attention span and intensity of focus ('in the zone')

Verbal skills (speaking, listening, reading, writing)

Non-verbal skills (visual gestures, body language, touch)

Cognitive (thinking) skills

We are born struggling to make sense of our world and relying on others to make decisions for us, unless we learn how to work out how to solve problems we cannot succeed. We must develop good

Analytical thinking – to understand 'cause and effect' and detect the key information (factors) for our decision.

Conceptual thinking – to put this information into context so we are able to understand and relate information to our situation.

Self-awareness

We are born totally unaware of who or what we are, unless we learn our strength and weaknesses we cannot know what we need to learn to succeed. Poor development of this can result in serious mental problems (attachment theory) and low self- esteem.

Managing Feelings

We are born unable to control our impulses, learning how to manage our emotions ('delay gratification') is essential to humans being successful. We need to learn to achieve 'long term gain' despite 'short term pain'

Motivation

We will experience difficulties from the moment we are born and unless we learn from these setbacks and experiences we cannot become resilient and unprepared to try to overcome difficulties (succeed)

Empathy

Humans are 'social animals' and much of our motivation and pleasure involves relationships with others, and unless we learn to understand and appreciate how other people feel we cannot relate or benefit from them.

Social skills

Since 'relationships' are so important to us, unless we learn to handle a wide variety of relationships and deal effectively with them we are likely to feel lonely, rejected, frustrated, angry and unhappy. The quality of our life is greatly affected by how well we 'get on with' other people, and these skills will be key to our effectiveness and success. Our success usually depends on learning to become an effective leader and avoiding following other people's poor decisions.

Chapter 10
'Assessing The Skills Needed To Succeed'

Stacey and Suzi stood and admired their posters on the wall.

"Do you think you understand what they all mean, Suze?" Stacey asked.

"Just about, though some of those words are new to me like cognitive, analytical, conceptual, resilient, gratification, and empathy. If you do this 'Assessing the skills we need to succeed', it should help. Are you going to do it now?" Suzi responded.

"Yeah, I'll have a go, will you help me?" Stacey replied.

"Of course" Suzi was delighted to be asked and be able to help.

Both had copies that they'd downloaded and printed.

Assessing the skills we need to succeed

GRADES

10 – DEFINITELY/EXCELLENT-	IT OCCURS ALL OF THE TIME
8 – VERY GOOD –	IT OCCURS MOST OF THE TIME
6 – FAIRLY GOOD –	IT OCCURS SOME OF THE TIME
4 – O.K.- -	IT OCCURS OCCASIONALLY
2 – VERY WEAK -	IT OCCURS RARELY
0 – NO –	IT DOES NOT OCCUR AT ALL

Effective Learning	Grade
Copes with challenges and change comfortably Readily develops new skills Learns effectively independently	1

Suzi sat on the bed, Stacey sat on the chair at the computer with the sheet on the desk and a pencil in her hand, and said.

"Right, let's start with 'Effective Learning'. I've never been able to cope with new challenges or develop new skills and learning without a lot of help has been impossible, so not a good start.

Communication	Grade
Concentrates intently despite distraction. Verbal skills (speaking, listening, reading, writing) Non-verbal skills (visual gestures, body language, touch)	1

Communication Grade Concentrates intently despite distraction.
Verbal skills (speaking, listening, reading, writing)
Non-verbal skills (visual gestures, body language, touch)1"Surely I'll be better on the 'Communication skills'. Arthur helped me understand this skill, these verbal skills are when we use words, particularly speaking and listening, I often misunderstand what people are saying and they don't understand me. Obviously, I'm rubbish at reading and writing. Non-verbal skills are visual gestures, body language and touch. I didn't understand these at all until Arthur explained it to me. We actually communicate loads of information by the tone of our voice and the expressions on our

face, as well as our body positions and what we do with our hands, arms and legs.

Arthur illustrated to me that I frequently 'sent out or picked up the wrong signals', apparently many of my problems with boys and their girl friends relates to this."

"Why don't we get taught anything about non-verbal skills in school, they seem very important?" Suzi asked.

Stacey immediately replied

"Excellent point, Suze, I've no idea, perhaps Drama is supposed to help with this. I learnt so little in school anyway that it wouldn't have helped me, anyway. I'm not doing very well on this assessment am I and I don't think this next skill will help, either."

Cognitive	Grade
Understands 'cause and effect' and detects the key information (factors) to make decisions (Analytical thinking) Puts information into context so is able to understand and relate information to the situation (Conceptual thinking) Able to recognise and make decisions that have very positive consequences.	1

"I've never heard of 'Cognitive skills' before, what's this one mean?"

Stacey answered.

"These are the skills we use to solve problems, it is what we use to refer to as 'intelligence'. This is what we are supposed to develop in school in maths and science. Unfortunately, I've not really done much of this over the years; I found them so boring so I just switched off. I've rarely tried to work out why things happen and I reckon I've rarely thought how we work out the result or conclusion to a problem using logic or 'common sense'. Furthermore I've almost never been able to make good decisions."

Self-awareness	Grade
Knows and accepts what they are feeling, and can label their feelings. Can identify their strengths and weaknesses, and feel positive about themselves. Can reflect on their actions and identify lessons to be learned from them.	0

Stacey continued.

"This next skill is 'Self-awareness', which is actually what I am practising now. I've begun to realise how confused I've been about my feelings. I've actually been blaming everyone for everything because I've been so frustrated and angry. Arthur has already helped me so much to understand myself more, and how little I actually know and accept my feelings.

I am obviously poor at identifying my strengths and weaknesses, and I certainly don't feel positive about myself. This assessment is showing how little I really know about myself and I suspect few people have done an assessment on these essential skills. I have probably never reflected on my actions and identified the lessons to be learned from them. Until Arthur visited me I don't think I've learnt any lessons from mine or others experiences and this process of reflection, what we're doing now, is virtually a first for me."

"The next skill is 'Managing Feelings'. I've spent much of my life avoiding showing emotions or trying to pretend I feel different to what I actually do, and I have never considered that my feelings can have a significant impact both on other people and on what happens to them. Now I think about it, this is incredibly stupid and selfish, since my behaviour clearly caused so many problems for others like you and mum and dad."

Suzi commented on this.

"I used to be frightened of what would happen when you came into the house, I stopped talking to you because you got so angry, didn't you realise that"

Stacey was clearly upset and said.

"No, it's appalling isn't it, but I've never thought of how my actions affected people and I've never found any strategies to manage my impulses and emotions."

Suzi added. "I suppose it's obvious that managing your feelings has not been a strength for you, sis"

Motivation	Grade
Can view errors as part of the normal learning process, and bounce back from disappointment or failure (Resilient) Can use their experiences, including mistakes and setbacks, to make appropriate changes to their plans and behaviours. Can take responsibility for their lives, believe that they can influence what happens to them and make wise choices. (Internal locus of control)	0

Stacey then responded.

"Yeah, that's a real understatement, and I suppose it leads on to the next skill, 'Motivation'. I spent my teenage years desperately avoiding doing anything that might result in failure and being totally crushed by any disappointments. I couldn't really cope with setbacks so learning from them has never really happened. I've been unable to take responsibility or make wise choices. Arthur demonstrated clearly that I try to blame everyone and anything for any problem I meet."

Empathy	Grade
Can work out how people are feeling through their words, body language, gestures, and tone. Can see the world from other people's emotions and points of view, taking into account their intentions, preferences and beliefs and can feel with and for them. Can shows respect (care and consideration) for people from diverse cultures and backgrounds, and for people with diverse interests, attainments, attitudes, and values, and they are interested in, enjoy and celebrate differences	0

Stacey then explained.

"Now this skill, 'Empathy' is about how well we understand others and I haven't got a clue what other's are feeling, I usually assume they are the same as me. I've not tried to see others views at all really, I think that's why I've bullied others so much. My lack of respect for you, mum and dad, let alone anybody else is pretty obvious so another very low score."

"You're being very hard on yourself, Sis". Suzi said, realising how low Stacey's overall score would be.

Stacey responded.

"Maybe, Suze, but Arthur's session with me made me aware that if I am to learn and change I must 'Start with the end in mind' and be clear where I am going and where I'm starting from."

Suzi didn't really understand Stacey's answer but didn't comment.

Stacey continued.

"The last essential skill is 'Social Skills', which ought to be a

Social Skills	Grade
Can work and learn well in groups, taking on different roles, cooperating with others to achieve a joint outcome. Can achieve an appropriate level of independence from others, charting and following their own course while maintaining positive relationships with others. Can give and receive feedback and use their experiences to help make decisions to improve their and other people's achievements	1

strength as I like being with my mates, but I've got a feeling it won't be. I've struggled to work with anyone so far and unable to cooperate with others has repeatedly been stated as a problem. Maintaining positive relationships with others has clearly been beyond me so far. I've not managed to have any long term close friends, boyfriends or jobs. I'm rubbish at taking criticism and praising others, or learning from them."

"So Stace, now you've finished it, do you want to know your overall score?" Suzi asked.

"It's not too difficult to add up, is it" Stacey commented.

"You've got 4 out of a possible 80" Suzi answered.

"It's pathetic, isn't it, no wonder I've struggled for all these years." Stacey commented.

"But what does it mean, Sis? Why haven't you learnt these skills?" Suzi asked. "How do you learn them? How can you learn them now?"

To which Stacey replied.

"Brilliant questions Suze, and I can't answer them. Arthur, gave me a brief outline about learning, and he said he would return to help me with this, so 'watch this space'. But I am now very aware of one thing I've got to try to do and that's find a way of learning these skills."

"Do we start watching 'Child of our time' now?" Suzi asked.

Stacey answered.

"Oh yeah, I'd forgotten about that. Perhaps it will help explain how we learn these skills. Make a space for me, and I'll set it up to watch".

Stacey sorted out the BBC website and set up programme 1, then moved to sit next to Suzi on the bed to watch it. Since the series began in the year 2000 and about three programmes have been made each year since then, there were many hours to watch, so the pair continued this for the rest of the day.

Name: *Stacey Smith*	Skills Needed To Succeed Report

GRADES
10 – DEFINITELY/EXCELLENT-   IT OCCURS ALL OF THE TIME
8 – VERY GOOD –   IT OCCURS MOST OF THE TIME
6 – FAIRLY GOOD –   IT OCCURS SOME OF THE TIME
4 – O.K.-   IT OCCURS OCCASIONALLY
2 – VERY WEAK -   IT OCCURS RARELY
0 – NO –   IT DOES NOT OCCUR AT ALL

ESSENTIAL SKILL	GRADE
Effective Learning - Copes with challenges and change comfortably, readily develops new skills and learns effectively independently	1
Communication skills – Concentrates intently despite distraction. Verbal skills (speaking, listening, reading, writing) Non-verbal skills (visual gestures, body language, touch)	1
Cognitive skills - Understands 'cause and effect' and detects the key information (factors) to make decisions (Analytical thinking) Puts information into context so is able to understand and relate information to the situation (Conceptual thinking) Able to recognise and make decisions that have very positive consequences.	1
Self-awareness - Knows and accepts what they are feeling, and can label their feelings. Can identify their strengths and weaknesses, and feel positive about themself. Can reflect on their actions and identify lessons to be learned from them.	0
Managing Feelings - Have a range of strategies for managing impulses and strong emotions such as anger, anxiety, stress and jealousy so that they do not lead them to behave in ways that would have negative consequences for them or for other people.	0
Motivation - Can view errors as part of the normal learning process, and bounce back from disappointment or failure.(Resilient) Can take responsibility for their lives, believe that they can influence what happens to them and make wise choices. (Internal locus of control)	0
Empathy - Can work out how people are feeling through their words, body language, gestures, and tone. Can see the world from other people's emotions and points of view, taking into account their intentions, preferences and beliefs and can feel with and for them.	0
Social skills – Can work and learn well in groups, taking on different roles, cooperating with others to achieve a joint outcome. Can give and receive feedback and use their experiences to help make decisions to improve their and other people's achievements.	1
General Summary	

Chapter 11
'How The Skills Are Learnt'

"You've had another good day, well done"
Stacey woke up suddenly with the sound of Arthur's voice.
"Oh hallo, I was really hoping you'd see me tonight." Stacey said promptly.
"Yes, I know. Don't worry I am aware of your thoughts and feelings as well as your actions. I know you now want to discover how these skills are learnt, why you haven't learnt them and how you can learn them now." Arthur replied.
"Exactly right, I think Suzi is keen to know the answers to those as well." Stacey responded.
"She is, you've begun a good job of helping Suzi learn, and as you will soon discover, trying to teach others is invariably the most effective way of trying to learn, so trying to teach Suzi is an excellent place to start. If you research 'The Learning Pyramid' on the computer, you will see that this clearly illustrates that the most effective method of learning is 'Teaching Others', and it will help you a great deal to refer to the pyramid regularly. I think you will also find it very helpful to research on your computer 'The 5 Learning Requirements', I showed you this before but I want to show you a different version this time."
Arthur pointed to the wall and this slide appeared.

The 5 Learning Requirements for Social and Emotional Skills

MOTIVATION	We are motivated to 'belong and feel attached', so we need people to regularly teach and MODEL THEM
CONCENTRATION (REFLECTION)	Opportunities and time to focus and reflect (think deeply) on our difficulties, experiences and feelings
ENVIRONMENT	Time and environments that allow us to observe, reflect and discuss our difficulties, experiences and feelings
ATTAINABLE TASKS	Tasks involving interaction with people to share difficulties, experiences and feelings eg. Games, hobbies, challenges, and team activities
FEELING SUCCESS	Experience the elation in overcoming difficulties, and the importance of encouragement or emotionally healthy constructive criticism

Arthur explained.

"The last five skills are called 'social and emotional' because that's what they particularly relate to. Throughout the 20th century, these skills weren't particularly focused upon in schools and society, and the importance of them to humans was relatively unknown. However, these skills are extremely essential to the success of humans, sometimes called 'Emotional Intelligence', and are now often poorly learnt, I will try to explain why."

The top row of the slide began glowing.

"Humans are desperately keen to bond with each other and demonstrating or modelling, their skills is a major step in helping people to learn them. For centuries, children learnt from their parents or people close to them, and so it was central to learning these skills. However, in the 21st century family life has changed a great deal and the reduced family interaction, together with the huge increase in media and celebrity personalities, means the role models have changed immensely. Most young people now seem to be confused as to who and what to follow, often choosing celebrities with a distinct lack of learning of these essential skills. For generations, children would learn the habits and behaviour of their parents; this still occurs but too often they are the habits and behaviours that parents don't want their children to learn."

"Stacey, your parents had no idea what you were learning, or how or why, and most parents are like this, so they did not deliberately model any of these 8 essential skills so whether you copied them was just by chance."

Stacey was fascinated already and asked at this point.

"I suppose very few parents actually know the skills their children need and so could not possibly deliberately model or demonstrate it to them."

Arthur then replied.

"Yes, that's true, though many cultures have developed traditions, behaviours, habits, rituals, manners etc that were usually introduced originally to model or demonstrate good behaviour and helped developed some of these skills in children. You grew up at a time when these traditions and rituals were occurring less and less, so they weren't being modelled and you weren't able to practise them."

Stacey's eyes showed she'd realised what Arthur was trying to convey and also it's importance and commented.

"I think I understand this, basically when we grow up we tend to copy our parents and how we behave is what we are taught."

Arthur responded to this.

"Well that's roughly the situation, but there are other things to consider. As you can see we need to be motivated to learn, so unless the child has a reason to learn they won't. Also we need to concentrate in order to learn, and parents will not know when their children are concentrating so won't always know what their child have observed. Furthermore, unless the environment is suitable the learning will also not occur, but if all these things are in place learning occurs even though the parents don't want it to."

"A common example of this is the words children often say are one's that their parents wish they didn't, this is because the child hears these words from emotionally charged parents, increasing the child's concentration and motivation so that they learn."

Stacey seemed to understand this and responded.

"This makes a lot of sense, so I will have learnt a lot of stuff from my parents that they wish I hadn't."

Arthur nodded and added.

"Absolutely, a lot of what children have learnt over the years has been down to chance, and you were born at a time when lots of distractions occur in the home, especially television. Therefore, the chances of young people learning what they really need have decreased a great deal."

"So is this why I haven't really learnt the 8 essential skills?" Stacey asked.

Arthur pointed to the wall and a video clip of Stacey as a toddler with her parents, in their early twenties, and said.

"I will again use some video clips to try to clarify this. This shows you nearly twenty years ago, your parents love you very much and are trying to do what's best for you. Unfortunately, they don't really know what to do and they are trying to provide you with a lot of material things like clothes and toys, because they're thinking that is what you need. Of course, you want to do only what you like doing and complain when you can't, and cause them a lot of trouble when you can't get your own way. Because your parents, like most, tended to 'give in' too easily and did not know what you really needed, they often just gave you what you wanted, so you were too often denied the opportunity to learn these skills."

"What do you mean 'denied the opportunity to learn these skills'?"

Stacey asked.

Arthur answered this.

"This is a very important part to understand. Here is a video clip of your granddad, Stan, your mother's father, my son as a child. He's only a toddler, about 2 years old in 1940; I am away, serving in the army in the Second World War. As you can see he's playing a game with his older sister, Sally, she's about 10 years old, whist my wife, Celia is doing the cooking, cleaning and washing. Stan is developing his skills from both his mother and his sister as they are interacting, doing things, with him and with each other. They are repeatedly talking to him, reading to him, playing with him, stopping him from doing things, and leaving him to play on his own."

"It is now about 8 years later, after the war, Stan is now 10 and Sally is 20, I and my wife are all having our evening tea together, chatting with each other and then playing cards together."

"We now move on about 10 years, Sally is now a mother, and that's Stan now 20 playing with his nephew, Sally's daughter Susan, about 2 years old. This is 1958, but notice how similar the house and the family are to the one you saw in 1940. There are still lots and lots of interaction and support for each other."

"We now return to about 1990, with you and your parents, do you see the difference, you are watching television, and nobody is interacting with you."

"Now 5 years later, you are again watching television, still no interaction, another 5 years and you are 10, you are either watching television, playing on your playstation, or playing on your computer, still no interaction."

Stacey was clearly amazed and commented.

"It's incredible, it seems until I was born families and homes remained unchanged".

Arthur responded to this comment.

"That's not entirely correct, this is your mother, aged about 5 years old in 1973, she's watching television with her parents, already the changing family and house structure is occurring, though very few channels are available, only a few hours of children's programmes and no recording devices."

Stacey was confused and asked.

"But why does this make so much difference, how does this affect the development of the essential skills so much?"

Arthur went on to explain.

"Learning skills takes a lot of time and practice, hundreds and thousands of hours of practice to really develop them. Consider learning to speak, read, write, catch, throw, kick, drive etc. these are relatively simple skills, but they need many hours of practice, the 8 skills we need to succeed are much more complex and need many more hours of practice. Furthermore, the practice for these requires tasks involving interaction with people to share difficulties, experiences and feelings e.g. games, hobbies, challenges, and team activities, which you rarely ever did."

"The situation becomes even worse, because these skills require people to have opportunities and time to focus and reflect, think deeply, on their difficulties, experiences and feelings and then to feel the elation, the success, in overcoming these difficulties, This also means they need to have a great deal of encouragement and healthy constructive criticism to help them succeed."

"Stacey, you had what is now a typical home life until the age of 11, which means most of this was missing from your life, so at that age your development of these essential skills was very poor."

Stacey was clearly very concerned and asked.

"So were my mum and dad, 'bad parents'?"

Arthur replied.

"It would be very unfair to label them as bad parents, not very effective would be a better description and that was because they didn't know what was needed to be effective".

Stacey then responded.

"But if mine was a typical home life, why aren't there more young people like me?"

Arthur again explained.

"You've forgotten some of the stuff I showed you on the first night. There are more and more young people like you, with very similar problems. You are no longer an exception; the majority of children are growing up with poorly developed skills. Suzi is one of them"

Stacey's face showed she had recalled it, and said.

"Oh yes, I remember it now, so how can I help Suzi develop them, and how can I develop them now".

Arthur responded.

"That's for another night, I think you've got enough to consider. Don't forget to research 'The Learning Pyramid' and 'The 5 Learning Requirements'. I'll see you soon, good-bye"

Arthur raised his arm and disappeared into the blinding white light behind him as he had done before.

Stacey could now hear a tapping noise, and as her eyes opened she could hear a voice.

"Are you awake? Sis, are you awake yet?"

It was Suzi, gently tapping on Stacey's bedroom door. The 'old' Stacey would've shouted and sworn at this 'intrusion into her 'precious sleep', but 'that was then, and this is now', and she was excited at the prospect of being able to tell Suzi about Arthur's latest visit.

"Come in. Suze, I'm awake, just" Stacey said enthusiastically.

Suzi's excitement was etched all over her face.

"Morning Sis, well, did he visit?" Suzi asked immediately.

"Yep, and he's answered one of our questions." Stacey replied as she pushed herself up in her bed so that she was sitting upright. She tapped the space next to her to invite Suzi to sit there, which Suzi did straightaway.

"What you doing, what you writing" Suzi asked as Stacey picked up the pen and pad next to her bed.

"The Learning Pyramid' and 'The 5 Learning Requirements', they are the 2 things Arthur asked me to research." Stacey answered.

"Never heard of them, what's their link with our questions?" Suzi asked.

"They help to explain how we learn and they particularly help to explain how the 8 essential skills are learnt. He also showed me some more video clips on that wall." Stacey replied.

Stacey pointed to the bedroom wall that they now call 'The Video Wall', and continued her description.

"I saw clips of granddad Stan as a young child in the forties and fifties, mum as a child in the seventies and me, when I was a toddler in the nineties. He showed how different family life was in the 'olden days' compared to now or when I was little."

"Why, what was the point of that?" Suzi asked.

"Our lives are dominated by television and electronic stuff, their lives involved listening, talking and playing with people. They continually practised the 8 essential skills when they were growing up; we don't, so we grow up without really learning the skills we need to succeed.". Stacey responded.

"Well that explains your terrible score yesterday", commented Suzi.

Stacey added. "Arthur mentioned you, Suze. He pointed out that you're growing up, not developing these skills, I think he wants me to help you learn them."

"Oh please, Sis. Would you do that, I don't want all these problems when I'm a teenager, help me please, please"

Suzi pleaded and was clearly worried.

"I'll try, one of the reasons for finding out about 'The Learning Pyramid', is that Arthur said the most effective way of learning is to 'Teach Others', so I think he's keen for me to try to help you. I suppose we'd better get up and get on with it, then."

Stacey's voice displayed an enthusiasm that had been very rare for a long time.

"Do you know what day it is Sis? Suzi asked.

"Er no". Stacey said and thought for a few seconds. "Christmas Eve, this is a very strange Christmas, nothing like any I've had before."

"I've already had my best ever Christmas present." Suzi commented.

"What's that?" Stacey asked.

"You - a brand new big sister to replace that horrible creature who used to be here!" Suzi replied immediately.

Stacey's eyes started to water, a lump appeared in her throat, and she gave Suzi a huge hug.

"What a lovely thing to say" The lump in Stacey's throat almost prevented her from speaking. "I'm so sorry for who I've been, I promise I'll make it up to you. Come on let's get up and get on with it."

Both Stacey and Suzi were not used to feeling or behaving like this and so found it uncomfortable but very pleasing. They got up briskly and started to prepare for their day together.

Chapter 12
'Our technology has exceeded our humanity'

"I like this picture of the Learning Pyramid, you can read the words clearly" Stacey commented as she studied a picture on the internet.

"It's a bit small, but we could make a good poster from it" Suzi replied.

"Excellent idea, Suze, I'll print it off and you can start while I look for 'The Five Learning Requirements".

Suzi already had a large white sheet of paper on the floor of Stacey's bedroom, with a biscuit tin full of coloured felt pens on it. Stacey was sitting at her computer, scrolling through pages on the screen. The picture of the Learning Pyramid slowly came out of the printer and Suzi stretched over to remove it.

The Learning Pyramid

This diagram shows the average retention rates for different styles of learning. The styles at the top show the least effective and on average how much is learnt.

Lecture 5%

Reading 10%

Audio Visual 20%

Demonstration 30%

Discussion Group 50%

Practice By Doing 75%

Teaching Others 90%

Source: National Training Laboratories, Bethel, Maine

"Have you seen this before Sis, its amazing?" Suzi was clearly excited by it.

"Not really." Stacey replied. "Arthur showed a huge slide of it on the wall when he first visited me, but I can't really remember it. Why, what's amazing about it?"

"Well it shows that the poorest ways of learning is 'Lecturing', which is when the teacher is standing at the front of the class telling you stuff. My teacher does that all the time". Suzi answered.

"You wait 'til next year, when you go to secondary school, you get loads of that, I hated it when I was at school, it was so boring and I couldn't remember or understand anything." Stacey promptly replied.

"The next worst is 'Reading', and we do loads of that. I'm terrible at that, no wonder I don't learn anything," Suzi commented.

"Again, next year they expect you to do even more of that, especially for homework." Stacey responded. "It used to take absolutely ages to read anything, and then I couldn't understand it. I didn't even understand the questions most of the time let alone attempt it. I never learnt anything from the homeworks I was given."

"That's exactly what it shows, the most commonly used methods of learning are the poorest" Suzi added. "The most effective one is 'Teaching Others', that's what we've been doing for the last few days, I've learnt loads like this, what about you Sis?"

"I've not only learnt loads, I've enjoyed it as well. Arthur said this is the best way to learn and he's right. We never did this at school; the teachers wouldn't even let us talk to each other, let alone help each other." Stacey replied.

"Will you help me prepare for my SATs next year, Sis?" Suzi asked.

"Now that's an interesting question Suze, 'cos Arthur showed me the 'Skilful Stacey' becoming really good at exams using something called 'Superlearning'. Perhaps he'll explain it to me a bit more at some time and we can both use it." Stacey answered.

"Sounds good, OK" Suzi responded.

"What I could do Suze, if you want, try to complete this 'Essential Skills Report' with you, like we did on me yesterday. Arthur clearly wants me to help you learn these skills, and he reckons that you, like me, will not be very good at them." Stacey suggested.

"Yes, please. I was thinking yesterday when we did that assessment on you together, that I'm not very good at these either. Can we do it now?" Suzi requested.

"Yeah, OK. We'll do that, and then make the posters of the Learning Pyramid and the 5 Learning Requirements." Stacey replied.

Suzi went and sat on Stacey's bed, Stacey got out the report they'd printed off yesterday and started reading out the description in the first box.

"Effective Learning - copes with challenges and change comfortably, readily develops new skills and learns effectively independently. Are you any good at this, Suze?" Stacey asked.

"I don't know really, I don't think so. Mum and Dad might know." Suzi replied.

"Perhaps we should do it with their help. I've just realised I don't really know much about you, I've had so little to do with you over the years." Stacey said as her eyes started to water again and for the second time that day, a 'lump appeared in her throat'.

"I'm so sorry, Suze. I don't even know my own sister" Stacey just about managed to say.

"It's alright Sis. You're making up for it now." Suzi said and also started to have tears form in her eyes, so got up off the bed and hugged her older sister sitting in the computer chair.

"We'll see if we can get Mum and Dad's help over tea. We'll get back to making the posters." Suzi commented.

"Good idea, Suze. We'll do that. I'll show you and explain this stuff on the 5 Learning Requirements."

Stacey said as she put down the report and picked up the printout of the 5 Learning Requirements, and continued.

"The first requirement is 'Motivation', we can't learn anything unless there is a good reason for it. It mentions in this explanation something about 'Maslow's Hierarchy', I've never heard of it, we'll have to find out more about this."

"The second one is 'Concentration', apparently our brain must be 'tuned into' the information being given out and think deeply or reflect on it, so that it becomes imprinted or embedded in the brain."

"The third one is 'Environment', and this means that for our brain to get this 'imprint', there needs to be few distractions and the climate to learn needs to be right. An example given here, is when you start to learn to drive there must be no other traffic or worries about anything apart from the accelerator and brake pedals."

"They continue using this example for the fourth one 'Attainable Tasks', and point out that each step must not be too large. So once the control off the accelerator and brake pedals have been mastered, the clutch pedal should then be considered, followed by the gear lever and so on. It points out that if when each step or task has been learnt, we 'Feel Success' and motivated to move on to the next task or step.

'Feeling Success' is the fifth and final learning requirement, because we're back to motivation then. It all makes a lot of sense to me, does it to you, Suze?"

(see diagram next page)

"Yeah, it does. I was thinking about when I was learning to ride a bike. Dad took me out on to the street with my new bike on a cold, windy day a few Christmases ago; I couldn't ride it at all. In fact, I fell over, hurt my knee and got really upset and didn't touch the bike until the summer. We went to the park on a nice sunny day, and I learnt to ride the bike easily on the short flat grass, 'cos I didn't hurt my knee when I fell over". Suzi explained.

"That's a brilliant example Suze. It fits these learning requirements perfectly." Stacey commented.

"Again, I don't understand why we haven't had any of this at school. It's all so helpful." Suzi asked.

"No, I haven't a clue either, Suze. I'm sure it would've helped me when I was at school". Stacey responded.

THE FIVE LEARNING REQUIREMENTS

Whatever you are trying to learn you need the following:

MOTIVATION	Unless we are keen to learn, we will lack the determination to overcome the difficulties that will occur.
CONCENTRATION	If we do not focus on the task, our brain cannot receive or store the information needed.
ENVIRONMENT	Distractions can cause concentration to become too difficult to allow us to learn.
ATTAINABLE TASKS	Unless the task to be learnt is broken down into small steps ('bitesize chunks') they are too difficult to grasp ('too large to digest').
FEELING SUCCESS	If we do not feel we are making progress it becomes too difficult to keep motivated.

"So how do these learning requirements link with the 8 essential skills?" Suzi asked.

"Ah, I've found the table that Arthur showed me on his slide. It's helped remind me of his explanation. Unfortunately, I can't show video clips like he did, but I'll have a go." Stacey said and continued.

"Apparently this 'Maslow's Hierarchy' is very important with the first learning requirement here, 'Motivation' but the gist of it is our motivation to learn these skills is provided by the people around us. We are born depending on people, usually our parents and immediately start copying them. It seems we are being taught these skills all the time because people are demonstrating them, 'Modelling them' was how Arthur described it. Usually we want to learn these skills to be like them or to impress them. This is why although our concentration is not good when we are born, it can improve quickly if these learning requirements are applied. If we get lots of attention and lots of practice to learn to concentrate when we are very young our brains develop this 'deep imprint' and we can develop good concentration skills."

"It seems me and you Suze, didn't have this when we were babies and toddlers, so our skills of concentration are not well developed. According to Arthur and this article, the introduction of television and technology means our family members don't provide as much attention and practice as they used to in his day. Since all learning requires concentration, if this skill is not developed early, the other skills become more difficult to develop. You can probably see the importance of the right environment for babies to learn communication skills, and this is another example that both Arthur and this article refer to, that has declined with the increase in technology."

"Apparently, there is far less talking to babies and young children occurring nowadays so their listening and speaking skills are slower to develop."

Suzi then interrupted by asking. "So, basically because we now have loads of television channels, computers, DVDs, internet and stuff, parents aren't spending as much time with their children."

Stacey answered. "Not just parents. Arthur showed me examples of brothers and sisters playing with young children in the olden days. I've spent almost no time with you, which is why I couldn't do the report. I've spent most of your life watching television, films or on the computer. Apparently before television families used to spend loads of time playing games, making things, doing hobbies, reading to each other and talking".

"We never do any of those" Suzi commented.

"No, I know". Stacey commented. "The video clips Arthur showed me, had little children being 'told off' during these activities and older people showing them what to do and how to play. You don't get any of that, neither did I, no wonder we've not learnt how to learn effectively, or manage our emotions or understand and get on with each other."

"I would've loved to have done all those things with you and mum and dad, why didn't it happen?" Suzi asked.

"Our family is a typical one". Stacey replied. "Everyone is too involved in other things and we didn't know how important all these activities are, so they just didn't happen for you or me. In fact, it seems that these things occur in very few families these days. If we now look at the last learning requirement, 'Feeling Success', you and I haven't had many opportunities to experience setbacks and success and talk about with mum and dad or even each other, so how could we have developed our motivation skills, we've had almost no practice of it, no wonder we're rubbish at it."

Mum and dad won't know about any of this, will they Sis?" Suzi questioned.

"Almost certainly not. According to Arthur very few parents do, at the moment." Stacey replied. "I think we should try to tell them over Christmas and New Year, so that that we can all try to help you develop these essential skills."

"Definitely, but how is this going to happen, how are you going to learn these skills" Suzi asked.

"That's precisely what I asked Arthur, but he said I'd have to wait for another visit for that. Mind you, I've already got a few ideas from these discussions." Stacey responded. "I've also discovered a great quote from Albert Einstein which I think illustrates what has happened, perhaps we can make a poster of it and try to finish the others now and then take the report downstairs to do with mum and dad over tea."

> # "It has become appallingly obvious that our technology has exceeded our humanity."
> **Albert Einstein**

Suzi stared at the quote and commented.

"I think I understand it, 'our humanity' means the development of the skills that are essential to humans has been replaced by our electronic gadgets."

"I'm very impressed you understood it Suze, perhaps we're learning so much because we're teaching each other" Said Stacey.

Chapter 13
'Probably The Most Difficult Job In the World'

"It still seems too good to be true, after all these years of trying to live with 'the creature from the black lagoon', I still keep thinking this new personality will disappear and the old one returns" said Stacey's father (Steve)

"Don't worry, dad, she won't, she's gone for good." Stacey replied.

Stacey, Suzi, Steve and Sheila (mother) had just finished eating tea.

"I know how your dad feels though Stace, we've had so many years of problems, having you and Suzi sitting here with us on Christmas Eve, is amazing, just so difficult to believe." Said mum

"I know mum, I'm so sorry. I can't turn back the clock but at least I can do as much as I can to make things better in the future, especially to help Suzi." Stacey commented.

"What do you mean, 'help Suzi'?" Dad asked.

"Suzi and I have been doing lots of studying over the last few days and we think we know why I have had so many difficulties. We've discovered an assessment of the skills that we need to succeed and I'm not very good at any of them. Suzi wanted it to be done on her, but I couldn't do it because I don't know her well enough. We wondered if you'd both help her to complete it." Stacey asked.

"I'm fascinated to find out what these skills we need to succeed might be, sure we'll help." Dad replied.

Stacey got out a couple of copies of the report from the folder she'd brought downstairs with her and placed them on the table so that they could all see the statements on it.

Name: *Suzi Smith*	Skills Needed To Succeed Report

GRADES
10 – DEFINITELY/EXCELLENT-   IT OCCURS ALL OF THE TIME
8 – VERY GOOD –   IT OCCURS MOST OF THE TIME
6 – FAIRLY GOOD –   IT OCCURS SOME OF THE TIME
4 – O.K.-   ·   IT OCCURS OCCASIONALLY
2 – VERY WEAK -   IT OCCURS RARELY
0 – NO –   IT DOES NOT OCCUR AT ALL

ESSENTIAL SKILL	GRADE
Effective Learning - Copes with challenges and change comfortably, readily develops new skills and learns effectively independently	0
Communication skills – Concentrates intently despite distraction. Verbal skills (speaking, listening, reading, writing) Non-verbal skills (visual gestures, body language, touch)	1
Cognitive skills - Understands 'cause and effect' and detects the key information (factors) to make decisions (Analytical thinking) Puts information into context so is able to understand and relate information to the situation (Conceptual thinking) Able to recognise and make decisions that have very positive consequences.	1
Self-awareness - Knows and accepts what they are feeling, and can label their feelings. Can identify their strengths and weaknesses, and feel positive about themself. Can reflect on their actions and identify lessons to be learned from them.	1
Managing Feelings - Have a range of strategies for managing impulses and strong emotions such as anger, anxiety, stress and jealousy so that they do not lead them to behave in ways that would have negative consequences for them or for other people.	1
Motivation - Can view errors as part of the normal learning process, and bounce back from disappointment or failure.(Resilient) Can take responsibility for their lives, believe that they can influence what happens to them and make wise choices. (Internal locus of control)	0
Empathy - Can work out how people are feeling through their words, body language, gestures, and tone. Can see the world from other people's emotions and points of view, taking into account their intentions, preferences and beliefs and can feel with and for them.	0
Social skills – Can work and learn well in groups, taking on different roles, cooperating with others to achieve a joint outcome. Can give and receive feedback and use their experiences to help make decisions to improve their and other people's achievements.	1
General Summary	

"There's only 8 skills on it, is that all we need to succeed?" Dad asked.

"It appears so, dad. But it seems they aren't very well learnt by most people these days and that's why so many young people have so many problems." Stacey commented.

"Well there's no denying that large numbers of young people have many problems, you can't watch the news or pick up a paper without seeing problems relating to young people. So you're saying we know why now, do we?" Dad asked.

"Well, basically if we go through this assessment of these skills it may help". Stacey replied

Stacey continued.

"Here's the first one, 'Effective Learning' - Copes with challenges and change comfortably, readily develops new skills and learns effectively independently. Suzi is only 10 years old, so she's not going to be very good at that, but I don't think I'm a very good learner either."

"Well you're both better learners than I am, I find learning new things really difficult." Mum commented.

"But it was less important in the past, because the world wasn't changing so fast. In the 21st century, if you can't learn continually throughout your life you're stuffed!" Stacey replied.

"That's very true, Stace. We weren't taught how to learn, we were just fed loads of information, most of it useless. I reckon most of our generation will be poor at that." Dad remarked.

"Not only your generation, dad. I scored poorly on it." Stacey replied. "In fact I barely scored anything on any of them."

For the next hour, the four of them went through all eight skills and eventually had the report completed on Suzi with a total score of 5 out of a possible 80. However, more importantly the discussions between them revealed a similar score for mum and dad as well.

"This has been fascinating, Stace. Where did you get this analysis?" Dad asked.

Stacey took out another sheet from her folder and spoke.

"Suzi and I found it on the internet, with this article. Apparently, over the last 30 or more years there's been vast quantities of research into success and what's needed to achieve it. For the last few years, successful people and leaders have been identified as having these 8 skills being well developed and so it is now broadly accepted that to succeed we must have these skills developed quite well. It seems that in nurseries, primary and secondary schools in the future will focus on developing these skills. However, traditionally most of the development of these skills has probably occurred mainly in homes and communities, not in schools. But if young people in the future are to develop these skills, everyone who is involved with children and young people need to be aware of them and help with their development, especially parents."

Both parents were clearly very interested and dad responded immediately.

"I've never heard of this stuff before, but it seems to make so much sense. So the reason that so many kids these days seem to have problems is because most don't learn these skills very well. But why has that occurred in recent years?"

Stacey began to explain this. "Basically, life as a child growing up years ago used to be very different. When your parents were children they didn't have television and spent much of their time speaking, listening, reading and playing with their parents, other family members and friends. This meant they were practising these 8 skills all day and everyday."

Both parents looked at the reports in front of them and Mum spoke first.

"My mum still spends loads of time saying 'how different and much better things were in the old days'. I've never really understood this, because they had so few of the things that me and your dad have and nothing like the amount of stuff you and Suzi have."

This prompted Stacey to pull another sheet from her folder which had the title 'When I Was 12', and placed it on the table between her mum and dad.

When I Was 12

How many of the list below did you have when you were a 12 year old child?

1	Colour T.V.	27	Internet
2	Portable T.V.s	28	Satellite T.V.
3	Video recorder	29	Remote controls
4	DVD player	30	Digital watches
5	Stereo player	31	Electronic calculator
6	Cassette recorder	32	House telephone
7	CD player	33	Mobile telephone
8	Automatic washer	34	Family car
9	Tumble dryer	35	Holidays abroad
10	Electric Toaster	36	Cash machines
11	Electric kettle	37	Credit cards
12	Electric blender	38	Large supermarkets
13	Refrigerator	39	Shopping malls
14	Freezer	40	Leisure/fitness centres
15	Microwave	41	McDonalds
16	Dishwasher	42	KFC
17	Electric iron	43	Pizza Hut
18	Electric vacuum cleaner	44	Designer ('label') clothes
19	Shower	45	Video shops
20	Electric hairdryer	46	Contact lenses
21	Central heating	47	Weekly Live football on TV
22	Double glazing	48	Father 'out of work'
23	Duvets	49	Mother 'in work'
24	Computer	50	Meals in front of the T.V.
25	Video games	51	Allowance ('money for nothing')
26	e-mail	52	'Lifts to school'

They both studied it, and dad commented.

Dad responded. "This looks very interesting; perhaps we could all have a go at this tomorrow, when Grandma and Nan are here. I'd like to know their views on all of this"

They all thought this was an excellent idea and a great activity for Christmas day.

"Does anyone fancy watching 'Its A Wonderful Life'; we've got it on DVD" Suzi suggested with a huge smile towards Stacey.

"Ooh, that's my favourite film." Said mum.

"We know mum, that's a great suggestion, Suze." Stacey commented.

All four of them (Stacey, Suzi, mum and dad) went into the front room and watched the film, all struggling to hold back the tears at the end. They all went to bed on that Christmas Eve feeling it was an extremely special one.

Arthur did not visit Stacey that night, but Stacey and Suzi both were still excited when they woke up, it was Christmas morning, after all, and opened a number of their presents. Probably for the first time ever, Stacey got huge pleasure at seeing the delight on her sisters' face and realised she'd missed these opportunities in the past because of her selfishness.

The two girls then sifted through the various articles they'd printed off previously and then printed off a few more. By the time they'd both got ready and gone downstairs, their Gran (their mother's mum) Sarah and Nan (their father's mum) Angela had both arrived. They all chatted for a long time, apart from mum who was cooking the Christmas dinner. When they sat down for dinner Nan commented.

"I know you are not particularly religious, but I would like to say a huge thank you to God for bringing our Stacey back to us. To have our own 'prodigal daughter' with us at Christmas is a truly wonderful present."

Gran muttered. "Amen."

"What's a prodigal daughter" Suzi asked.

"In the Bible, there's a story about a son who becomes lost to his family and then when he returns they feel great joy. It's actually a parable called 'The Prodigal Son" Explained Nan.

"Well, I must say I've probably felt more joy than ever before when my wonderful sister replaced that 'thing' who used to live here, so I agree with that" Said Suzi.

Stacey looked very embarrassed and mum was clearly about to cry so she said.

"Come on, tuck in, dinner's getting cold."

They proceeded to eat Christmas dinner.

"When we've finished Gran and Nan, we'd like to you to have a go at a little survey that Suzi and I have found, about when you were growing up." Stacey commented.

"Oh, that sounds interesting, I'd like that" Nan responded.

"So would I" Gran commented.

So after dinner was finished, all six of them went into the front room, and Stacey gave out copies of the 'When I was 12' sheet to everyone and a pen, and they all attempted it.

There was a lot of laughing and chuckling.

"I haven't got any, I don't think I had any of these in 1956 when I was 12". Nan said first.

"I think I've got one, a vacuum cleaner, in 1958," said Gran.

"In 1980, I had about 18." Said Dad.

"And I had 19, in the same year" Said Mum.

"I had all of them" Stacey commented.

"Well, I'm not 12 yet" Suzi commented and they all laughed.

"What's the point of it, though, Stacey?" Nan asked.

"Suzi and I have spent several days looking at why I and other young people have had so many problems and we've discovered that it's almost certainly because we are brought up in a house, family and world that doesn't help us learn the essential skills we need to succeed." Stacey explained.

"What skills are these, Stacey?" Gran asked.

"They're on here." Stacey said as she gave out copies of the report that she'd completed on herself a few days ago.

"We had a great discussion last night when we attempted to complete an assessment like this, we all scored very poorly." Dad said. "It helped us understand that our kids grow up in a completely different world to me and Mum, and very much different to yours."

Nan studied the sheet and remarked.

"Ah, I think I'm seeing your point. Apart from 'Effective Learning and Cognitive', they are things we did all the time when we were kids, didn't we Sarah?"

"Yes, some of those statements were just what we did all the time as kids, we had to if we were to survive, especially as girls. We chatted, read and played all the time when we were little." Gran (Sarah) responded

Nan then commented. "Then we had to do jobs much of the time, as we got older, meet lots of people, travel all over the place, scrimp and save to buy things. I've never thought about it before, but I suppose we did grow up learning these 'skills', as you refer to them."

Stacey then responded to this.

"Kids today don't do these things. Suzi and I found an article on the internet that I think you and Gran will like, here have a look at this."

Stacey took out a few more sheets from her folder and gave them out to her parents and grandparents.

GROWING UP IN A DIFFERENT WORLD

- According to today's regulators and bureaucrats, those of us who were kids in the 70's and early 80's probably
- shouldn't have survived, because:
- Our baby cots were covered with brightly coloured lead-based paint which was promptly chewed and licked.
- We had no childproof lids on medicine bottles, or latches on doors or cabinets and it was fine to play with pans.
- When we rode our bikes, we wore no helmets, just plimsolls and lolly sticks in our wheels.

- As children, we would ride in cars with no seat belts or air-bags – riding in the passenger seat was a treat.
- We drank water from the garden hose and not from a bottle and it tasted the same.
  We ate chips, bread and butter pudding and drank fizzy pop with sugar in it, but we were never overweight because we were always outside playing.
- We shared one drink with four friends, from one bottle or can and no-one actually died from this.
- We would spend hours building go-carts out of scraps and then went top speed down the hill, only to find out we
- forgot the brakes.
- After running into stinging nettles a few times, we learned to solve the problem.
- We would leave home in the morning and play all day, as long as we were back before it got dark. No one was able to reach us and no one minded.
- We did not have Play stations or X-Boxes, no video games at all.
- No 99 channels on TV, no videotape movies, no surround sound, no mobile phones, no personal computers, no
- Internet chat rooms.
- We had friends, we went outside and found them.
- We played cannon and street rounder's, and sometimes that ball really hurt.
- We fell out of trees, got cut and broke bones but there were no law suits.
- We had full on fist fights but no prosecution followed from other parents.
- We played knock-and-run and were actually afraid of the owners catching us
- We walked to friend's homes. We also, believe it or not, WALKED or a BUS to school.
- We didn't rely on mummy or daddy to drive us to school, which was just round the corner.

- We made up games with sticks and tennis balls.
- We rode bikes in packs of 7 and wore our coats by only the hood.
- The idea of a parent bailing us out if we broke a law unheard of. they actually sided with the law.
- This generation has produced some of the best risk-takers and problem -solvers and inventors, ever.
- The past 50 years have been an explosion of innovation and new ideas.
- We had freedom, failure, success and responsibility, and we learned how to deal with it all.

All the adults laughed a great deal. Then Dad spoke.

"It's incredible how different the world was for us, even in the seventies, let alone the fifties when you were growing up, mum, compared to now. Sheila and I have been discussing it since our chat last night, we've been quite ashamed at how little we've been involved with Stacey and Suzi during their childhood."

Nan then replied.

"Steve, I don't think you've been bad parents, certainly no worse than most and better than many".

Gran also commented.

"We never had all the distractions that you've had. I just did what my parents and everyone else was doing. I can't say I really thought about it too much."

Mum then chipped in.

"I think that's why all this is so fascinating and important. Until last night, we never thought about these things before. We never really considered what Stacey and Suzi needed to learn when they were growing up, let alone knowing what these 'skills' are and how important they might be. But I don't think we've been any different to most parents, we've just been trying to do what we thought was best for our kids."

Dad then responded.

"We've been looking back, with all that's happened to Stacey, and considered why she's had all these problems, but until last night's discussion with Stacey and Suzi, we had no idea of what we should've done with her, and with Suzi."

Nan commented on this.

"I must admit, I would not like to be a parent now, it seems so difficult. It's not enough just to love them and believe your doing the right things. It's much more complicated than that now"

"You're not alone in thinking that, Nan. Have a look at this poster that we found on the internet. I think it demonstrates your point very well"

Stacey responded and showed them this poster.

They all studied it carefully and agreed.

Possibly the most difficult job in the world

-

Being a GOOD parent in the 21st century

Chapter 14
'The Incapable Generation'

"Parents today have my utmost sympathy." said Gran. "I've watched a lot of these reality television programmes where they have cameras in the home and I can't believe what happens. The kids are so rude and disrespectful, and the parents are almost as bad. Everyone is shouting at each other, the kids seem to do as they please, it's horrible"

"It used to be like that here" said Suzi. "In fact it was probably even worse than any of those programmes and Stacey was the 'teenager from Hell'."

"That's true, I'm so sorry, so very sorry". Stacey responded, her eyes watering as she said it.

"That's the past, Stace. What we must do is learn from it and make sure the future is better" Said Dad.

Nan also wanted to return to the topic of learning from the past and said. "But life was so very different when I was your age, Stacey. When I was 19, I had been working in a supermarket for 3 years, after having worked part time in a shop for 3 years before then. We didn't need all these qualifications that you do now to get a job."

"Actually Nan, you don't have to have lots of qualifications now to get jobs, especially since so many jobs now are dealing with customers." Said Suzi. "We found some very interesting stuff about jobs on the internet, which surprised us. Look at this."

Suzi opened the file and took out a sheet and gave it to her Nan, and another sheet to her Dad. "You haven't seen these either Dad or Mum".

The sheet showed the following article.

2005 National Employers Skills Survey – *The Learning Skills Council*
Skills lacking in order of importance

- **Teamwork**
- **Customer-handling skills**
- **Technical & Practical skills**
- **Oral communication**
- **Problem-solving skills**
- **Written communication**
- **Management skillsGeneral**
- **IT user skills**
- **Literacy skills**
- **Numeracy skills**

"According to this the most sought after skills are one's dealing with people, the exam stuff is down the bottom of the list" Nan commented.

"Those skills dealing with people, are 6 out of the 8 essential skills, they're called 'social and emotional skills.'" Stacey explained.

"Those 'social and emotional skills' are mentioned in this article,- look"

Gran showed everyone the article she had and read it out.

'In the 2004 Enterprise survey of 20,000 employers in the UK, employers were most worried about lack of skills such as customer handling, problem solving and teamworking. In fact, research has shown that social and emotional skills had more correlation with success in the labour market than cognitive skills, IQ and formal qualifications'
(Cunha et al., 2005).

"I'm amazed." Said Dad. "I had no idea that it is these skills that they keep going on about that our young people lack. Mind you, as a plumber for 20 years, the apprentices we get now are useless, they can't work with anyone, they're always moaning and arguing. They find everything 'too difficult and boring' and never show any initiative so I suppose it applies in my job"

"When I go into shops and in our supermarket, the assistants are hopeless. They don't seem able to listen to you, can't find anything, don't seem to care and are rude to you. I suppose that's why customer handling skills are in short supply." Mum commented.

"That's because most of us have spent the last 5 years communicating by mobiles, text, e-mail, and facebook. We hardly listen and talk to each other anymore, so young people aren't very good at it." Stacey observed. "There's a bit more to that article which makes this point further."

<u>The Incapable Generation</u>

'many young people today are left simply incapable of succeeding in the current socio-economic climate.'

'in just over a decade, personal and social skills or "capabilities" became 33 times more important in determining relative life chances'

"Freedom's Orphans"

Raising Youth In A Changing World – IPPR Research (Nov 2006) (page 2)

"These are fascinating articles, girls. That internet is a very clever thing." Nan commented.

"It certainly is, Nan. But I've not used it much for learning over the years, I've used it to watch videos, play games and communicate with my friends. I've only just realised how useful it is and how much I could learn from it. Suzi and I are determined that we do not become part of the 'Incapable Generation'. Stacey responded.

"So what do you intend to do then, Stacey" Gran asked.

"Suzi and I are going to do all that we can to develop the 8 essential skills." Stacey replied.

"How are you going to do that, then Stacey?" Nan asked.

"One thing Suzi and I would like, is to have discussions like this, with you, Gran, Mum and Dad. We've learnt so much in only a few hours and I've really enjoyed it". Stacey answered.

"So have I" Suzi agreed.

"I can't understand why we've not done this before; I've learnt loads as well." Dad commented.

"And I have" Mum said.

"Well we're all agreed on that then" Gran said.

"This has been like I remember Christmas as a child, I think this has been a wonderful start to Christmas, the best for many, many years" Nan concluded.

Chapter 15
The Family Forum

"It was wonderful to see you getting on so well with your Nan and Gran".

Stacey woke up immediately to the sound of that voice, it was Arthur!

"You really seemed to enjoy it and did a brilliant job at teaching them and your parents". He continued.

"I suppose I was teaching them, yes I did enjoy it, I never thought learning could be so much fun. Suzi's getting a real buzz from it as well." Stacey responded.

Arthur then said. "You now need to do some research on 'Motivation' to understand why. The last time I visited you, you wanted to discover how these skills are learnt, and how you can learn them now. I think you've already begun to answer these questions."

"What do you mean?" Stacey asked.

"During the last few days, you've clearly began learning effectively, the first and key essential skill. You've discovered the joy of learning and the effectiveness of the internet, and when you teach Suzi about 'SUPERlearning' you'll improve rapidly." Arthur commented.

"Teach Suzi about SUPERlearning?" Stacey asked.

"Yes, she's keen for you to help her prepare for her exams and when you've researched and taught her 'SUPERlearning' you will be an expert as well. This will also develop your 'cognitive skills', but already you've been trying to solve problems for yourself and attempting to make your own decisions. However, the most important process for learning these skills is shown in the 'Learning Pyramid', by teaching others. You've already discovered how effective this is in trying to teach Suzi, but importantly you've begun developing all these essential skills with the 'Family Forum' today."

"The 'Family Forum', what do you mean by that?" Stacey asked.

Arthur continued. "For centuries, humans have spent vast quantities of time discussing various topics. The early villages and then the communities in small towns often grew out of family life or worked together to survive, all using extensive discussions to overcome their difficulties. This meant everyone had lots and lots of practice at developing their communication, cognitive, self-awareness, managing emotions, motivation, empathy and social skills.

In the 21st century, this no longer really occurs and in-depth discussions on a wide range of important topics rarely occur. Yesterday, your discussions involving all your family, 'The Family Forum', gave an opportunity for you, Suzi and everyone to practise and develop all these skills. If you can regularly have these forums on a wide range of topics, you will improve immensely."

"I think we could do that, Nan, Gran, Mum and Dad, all seem to really enjoy it" Stacey replied enthusiastically.

"They've probably got lots of topics that they would like to discuss, prompted by the news and their concerns about the world today." Arthur replied. "Well that's enough for this short visit. It's time to for me to go. I'll see you soon, goodbye".

As usual, he departed by raising his arm and disappearing into the growing bright white light.

When Stacey woke up, she immediately scribbled on her pad; 'Motivation, SUPERlearning and Family Forum.'

It was Boxing Day, and with her Nan and Gran still staying with them so she thought it would be a great opportunity to suggest the 'Family Forum' to them, but first she wanted to mention it to Suzi.

"Arthur came again, only for a few minutes though, but he suggested we have 'Family Forums'."

Stacey said excitedly as she entered Suzi's bedroom.

"What's a 'Family Forum' and why should we have them?" Suzi asked.

"Basically, it's what we had yesterday with Nan, Gran, Mum and Dad, when we were discussing what causes people to be successful. Arthur said they are a great way of practising and developing the 8 essential skills."

Suzi was clearly excited and said.

"Well, I thought it was brilliant, it felt great knowing so much useful stuff and being able to help them learn. We've had a few lessons like this at school, not very often though. I think they were called 'Philosophy for Children' or 'Circle Time' or something. I really enjoyed them, we didn't do any writing but I learnt loads. I don't know why we only had a few of them. I'd love to have them at home. Do you reckon Nan, Gran, Mum and Dad would be interested?"

"I think so; we'll ask them at dinner." Stacey replied. "Arthur gave me 2 things to research on the internet, 'Motivation and SUPERlearning', do you want to help me?"

"Yes, I'd like that, you mentioned both of those the other day, and I'm hoping that SUPERlearning will help me with my SATs." Suzi responded.

"OK, let's get changed and we'll get going." Stacey said enthusiastically.

They both sprung up and set about sorting out clothes and went to get ready.

"I've found a diagram and article on 'Maslow's Hierarchy of Needs', it looks as though it's central to motivation. Here, I'm printing them off now, I'll explain it to you, and I think I understand it."

MASLOW'S HIERACHY OF NEEDS
This is what motivates us in life –

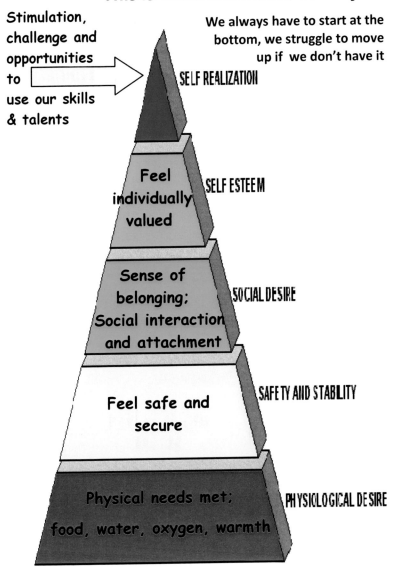

Stimulation, challenge and opportunities to [ ] use our skills & talents

We always have to start at the bottom, we struggle to move up if we don't have it

SELF REALIZATION

Feel individually valued — SELF ESTEEM

Sense of belonging; Social interaction and attachment — SOCIAL DESIRE

Feel safe and secure — SAFETY AND STABLITY

Physical needs met; food, water, oxygen, warmth — PHYSIOLOGICAL DESIRE

Stacey began her explanation.

"This diagram of 'Maslow's Hierarchy of Needs', is apparently now widely accepted and used as 'what motivates us'. It attempts to explain our 'needs and desires' starting at the bottom first and each one has to be achieved before this next one up applies. It makes a lot of sense. The first one is our health and physical needs. We need things such as oxygen, food, water, warmth etc. most and if we don't get them we would almost certainly die."

"Well, I suppose that's fairly obvious." Suzi commented.

Stacey continued.

"The second need or priority is to ensure that we feel safe and secure. We struggle to cope or concentrate if we feel insecure and it is particularly obvious in schools if we are frightened of being bullied. If we do feel safe and secure our third priority becomes relevant which is 'our sense of belonging'. This means we desire love, affection and attachment to people. Humans are 'social animals', we want to live and be in groups. We fear loneliness and being rejected by people, or from our family, community or a peer group."

"But you rejected us, your family for a long time, Stace" Suzi observed.

"I replaced that with my friends, peers and especially boyfriends. I've spent many years desperately trying to be accepted by them and failed completely." Stacey replied. "I think my actions and thinking was also influenced by the next, the fourth need or priority, 'Self-Esteem'. I think this is about how we see ourselves, what we think is important, our values. It says if these needs are not met, we feel inferior, weak, helpless and worthless. So we strive for a high level of self-respect, and respect from others in order to feel satisfied, self confident and valuable."

"I've heard 'Self-Esteem' used a lot, but I don't really understand it." Suzi commented.

"I'm not sure if I do, perhaps we should research this some more in the future." Stacey suggested.

"Good idea, I'll put it on your pad" Suzi replied.

Stacey continued. "The last one is 'Self- Realisation' which means we are 'devoted' and spend our time on something very important and precious to us. These things are sometimes referred to as our 'purpose, destiny, or vocation'. It seems few people tend to achieve this."

"So why did you become such an unpleasant person in your teens, then Stace?" Suzi asked.

"I think I desperately 'wanted to be part of a group' and feel accepted by other teenagers and behaved in a way to try to achieve this. But I'm going to study this a bit more if I can." Stacey answered.

"I think it's about time for dinner now, and we're going to ask if we can have 'Family Forums'. Suzi responded.

"It's amazing how quickly time passes when we're doing this stuff, I wonder if that's what this 'Self –Realisation' is about?". Stacey quizzed.

"Suzi and I have a request of you all" Stacey said as they all sat down at the dinner table. "At the end of yesterday's discussion, you all said how much you'd learnt and enjoyed it. Suzi and I wondered if we could have them frequently."

Stacey's Dad, spoke first. "Definitely, I found it and the one the day before fascinating. I was 'gobsmacked' at how much I learnt. I've been itching to find out how you people felt about a load of other topics."

"Me, as well". Mum said immediately. "I've spent so many years wondering what Stacey's been thinking and what the rest of you thought and felt yesterday was a real eye-opener".

"I know I'm not here all the time, but whenever I am I'd like that very much" Nan responded.

"Same goes for me. In fact I'd like to come over more frequently if we have them. I found it so enjoyable and interesting." Gran agreed.

"That's unanimous, then." Stacey said. "We'll call them, 'Family Forums', and we'll discuss any topic that any of us suggests, just like yesterday. If you can bring written information on the topic like me and Suzi did, that would be even better."

"OK, let's get on with dinner before it gets cold, and we can sort out what to discuss in our 'Family Forum' as you call it, after it." Mum suggested.

They all proceeded to dish up and tuck into their meal. As they were about to leave the table, Mum spoke to her mother.

"Yesterday's discussion, made me think of a poster that you gave me years ago, mum. Do you remember 'Children Learn What They Live'?"

"Yes, I do. I gave it to you when Stacey was born. Do you still have it?" Gran replied.

"I do, I've kept it in a drawer with the photos, since then." Mum answered.

"Sounds interesting, I don't remember ever seeing it. Can you get it please mum, perhaps we can have a 'Family Forum' about it?" Stacey asked.

Children Learn What They Live
By Dorothy Law Nolte

If children live with criticism,	*They learn to condemn*
If children live with hostility	*They learn to fight.*
If children live with ridicule,	*They learn to be shy.*
If children live with shame,	*They learn to feel guilty.*
If children live with encouragement,	*They learn confidence*
If children live with tolerance,	*They learn to be patient.*
If children live with praise,	*They learn to appreciate.*
If children live with acceptance,	*They learn to love.*
If children live with approval,	*They learn to like themselves.*
If children live with honesty,	*They learn truthfulness.*
If children live with security,	*They learn to have faith in themselves and others.*
If children live with friendliness,	*They learn the world is a nice place in which to live.*

Copyright © 1972/1975 by Dorothy Law Nolte

116

"That's why I mentioned it, Stace. It seemed to follow on from our discussion yesterday." Mum said and went upstairs to get the poster, while the others went into the front room.

Mum returned to the front room and gave the poster to her mum and it was then passed around the room. When Suzi looked at it she made the following comment.

"This is the first of the 'Five Learning Requirements', isn't it Stace?"

"Excellent point, Suze. You're right" Stacey replied.

"What's the 'Five Learning Requirements'? Dad asked.

"If we are to learn anything, there are 5 things that need to occur. We need to be motivated, we need to concentrate on what we're trying to learn. The environment needs to avoid having distractions and each step or task needs to be carefully planned so that they aren't too difficult to learn, then after each one we need to feel success so we keep on learning." Stacey explained.

"That makes a lot of sense, I'd like to know more about that in the future, but how does it relate to this poster, Suze?" Dad responded.

"The usual reason to learn is to copy or impress other people, especially the one's who matter most to us, like our parents. This poster seems to refer to this." Suzi replied

"I bought it years ago for that very reason, which must be almost 20 years ago. When I consider what we were talking about yesterday, it seems even more relevant now." Gran commented.

"When I was growing up, I had my family all around me most of the time. We played games all the time and I had the last eight things on the left hand side of the poster, especially from my dad, Arthur, he was such a great role model."

Suzi and Stacey looked at each other and smiled, feeling that they knew who Sarah was referring to.

"I thought of this yesterday, because I don't think I've been a particularly good role model to the girls". Gran remarked.

"But you've been better than me, Sheila. I feel ashamed at how little I've praised and encouraged the girls, I've criticised and lost my temper with them so much." Dad commented with a lump forming in his throat.

"Don't be too hard on yourself, Steve." Nan, his mother reassured him. "You didn't know how important all this was and how it would affect your kids. In our day, the father was always considered to be the breadwinner and disciplinarian, you were only doing what your dad and granddad had done. These ideas of the 'modern man' and parenting wasn't around 20 years ago, you just did what you thought was best, we decided on that yesterday. But it's never too late to change and Suzi is still only 10."

"I'd like to know more about this stuff. There's been lots of programmes on the telly about parenting, like 'Supernanny', 'Little Angels', Child of Our Time', that are about being better parents." Mum said.

"Me and Stace have been watching 'Child of our Time', mum." Suzi remarked.

"I didn't know it was on at the moment." Mum responded.

"We've been watching it online, on our computer. But we've only seen a few so far, they're still only babies, it's about 2001, in the ones we're watching" Suzi explained.

"I've not seen many of them, but they seemed interesting" Mum commented.

"I've watched them every year, I think they're excellent." Nan responded.

"So do I." Gran agreed.

"I've never heard of them. I can't bare the thought of watching programmes about badly behaved kids, especially the way Stacey's been over the last 10 years" Said Dad.

Stacey looked very embarrassed and wanted to apologise again, but her Dad continued.

"But, I think I should now, if I'm to learn what to do to help Suzi and possibly find out what I did wrong with Stacey."

"It sounds as if we could all do with learning about what it means to be a good parent and why all these kids are struggling." Nan interjected.

"That's what I thought when I found the poster". Said Mum.

"So in tomorrow's 'Family Forum' we will focus on 'Self-Esteem and Parenting'" Suggested Stacey, who had already decided to research 'Self-Esteem' anyway.

"OK, that's a great idea." Agreed Gran and everyone nodded in support.

Chapter 16
Self-Esteem and Positive Parenting

"Suze, I've found some interesting stuff on 'Self-Esteem', I think I understand why I was such a bitch throughout my teen years." Stacey exclaimed as she was sat at her computer.

Suzi was on Stacey's bedroom floor drawing a poster as they had done, the previous day. Suzi stopped and sat up to listen more carefully.

"I think this could be a useful poster, it seems to explain and summarise Self-Esteem' very well. What do you reckon?" Stacey said as she handed the printout to Suzi.

Self-Esteem is the **belief** that they are **capable** of overcoming difficulties in their lives to achieve success and happiness.

People with High Self-Esteem have a positive attitude to life and believe they are capable of overcoming the difficulties they meet. They are keen to take on new experiences, seeing them as challenges, not problems.

People with Low Self-Esteem have a negative attitude to life and do not feel they are responsible or can overcome their difficulties. They will often show the following characteristics:-

- Focus on trying to prove themselves or impress others.
- Tend to use or put down others for their own gain.
- May act with arrogance and contempt towards others.
- Repeatedly try to convince themselves of their worth.
- Reluctant to take risks to expose themselves to failure.
- Frequently blame others for their shortcomings rather than take responsibility for their actions.

Assessing Your Self Esteem 1

Read each statement and tick it if you feel it tends to apply to you

1. When I make mistakes I tend to either feel embarrassed, blame others if possible and claim   'I don't make mistakes' and desperately hope no one spotted it.
2. When I look at myself in the mirror, I tend to see
3. someone who is not very good at overcoming difficulties.
4. When I try to solve problems I tend to spend a lot of time and effort looking for who or what I think caused the situation and who to complain about.
5. If my views are different from those of others, I am likely to keep quiet or agree to avoid embarrassment.
6. When I think about the main aims in my life, I tend not to know what I should be doing or even where to start.
7. When I make a commitment to myself to change and improve I tend to fail to stick to it and return to my 'old ways'.
8. When I talk to myself, I tend to be very critical and negative, putting myself down and beating myself up emotionally.
9. When other people comment on my actions I tend to think they are saying something negative about me and take it very personally, or get defensive and often respond with a negative reaction to them.
10. I tend to gossip/talk about other people and readily discuss their faults.
11. I will always try to tell people what I've done or let them know my strengths.
12. Unless I feel I am very good at something I am unlikely to attempt it.

"I think I had very low Self-Esteem' throughout my teenage years, all those characteristics for low self-esteem applied to me. When

Arthur visited me the first time, he convinced me that it was my attitude, my belief that I had to change first. I was looking for an answer to my question 'What have I done to deserve this?' And he helped me realise that it was my negative approach that had basically caused my problems. If I believed that I could overcome my difficulties then perhaps I could overcome them. I have also discovered this self assessment on Self-Esteem, that's looks very useful."

Stacey added. "The assessment said that if you have no or just one tick you probably have good or high self esteem. Between 2 and 5 ticks you have average but fragile self esteem, more than 5 then you have low self esteem and I got 11 ticks!"

"I think we should use the other assessment with Nan, Gran, Mum and Dad, the one that focuses on high self esteem, I think it's more positive." Suzi suggested, comparing the 2 sheets she had in her hand.

"Yes, that's a good point, Suze." Stacey agreed.

"What do you think caused you to have such low self esteem, Stace?" Suzi asked.

Stacey replied. "I don't know at the moment, I think that's going to take a lot more research yet. But I have come across some stuff on parenting which may help and I think that poster Mum found has some clues in it. This stuff on parenting is called 'Positive Parenting' and apparently it's what 'Supernanny' and people on the telly tend to use. It seems modern effective approaches to parenting are based around this."

Stacey handed another sheet to Suzi.

(See top of next page)

"I'm very interested to see what Nan, Gran, Mum and Dad have to say about this." Suzi commented.

"And when they see this sheet that goes with it" Stacey responded and showed Suzi a sheet entitled 'How to increase conflict and create problems' and 'How to reduce conflict and problems".

"Right do you think we're ready, I think it's close to dinner time." Stacey asked Suzi, putting the sheets in her folder.

AN ENCOURAGED CHILD HAS NO NEED TO MISBEHAVE' (Rudolf Dreikurs)

The most effective way to change the behaviour of people, particularly children, is to use encouragement. The method of encouragement is dependent on the goal, aim or need behind the behaviour or action.

Goal	Child's Belief
Attention	"I count (belong) only when I'm being noticed or getting special service."
	"I'm only important when I'm keeping you busy with me."
Power	"I belong only when I'm boss or in control, or proving no one can boss me."
	"You can't make me."
Revenge	"I don't think I belong so I'll hurt others as I feel hurt."
	"I can't be liked or loved."
Inadequacy (Assumed)	"I don't believe I can belong, so I'll convince others not to expect anything of me."
	"I am helpless and unable; it's no use trying because I won't do it right."

The girls went downstairs and had dinner. As they were just about to finish dinner, Stacey spoke.

"Well, we've prepared some stuff for our 'Family Forum', you've all got a questionnaire to do on 'Self Esteem', and I hope you're all ready".

"I don't think I've done a questionnaire for years." Dad commented.

"Sounds great, let's go." Said Mum.

They all got up and moved into the front room where sat down in the armchairs and Stacey gave each of them a pen and a questionnaire. They immediately began reading and attempting to complete it.

Nan finished first and said. "I've only got 4 ticks".

Gran responded immediately. "Well I've only got 3".

Mum then answered. "I'm struggling to get any"

"And me" Said Dad. "What's the scoring system, then, Stacey".

"Well, they've got 2 versions, this one focuses on positive or high self esteem, I did one earlier which concentrated on low self-esteem. The scores for this one are:

5 or more ticks, high self esteem,

2 to 4 ticks, average self-esteem.

Less than 2 ticks, low self esteem."

"We don't seem to have good self esteem, then" Mum commented.

Nan quickly responded.

"I'm not surprised, though, if you consider the '8 essential skills we need to succeed' that we looked at the other day. Clearly, if we don't have those skills we are probably going to struggle to succeed and we probably won't have good self esteem."

"So what exactly is 'self esteem?" asked Mum.

"Here's this poster, I made that explains it" Suzi immediately replied and pulled out a poster from the folder.

"Self esteem is how much people believe they are able to overcome the difficulties in their lives so that they can achieve success and happiness, and people with high self esteem believe they can overcome the difficulties they meet and not phased by setbacks or new experiences." Suzi stated.

Mum then commented.

"I was really impressed with the stuff about the skills we need to succeed, and it helped me understand why so many people struggle. If young people aren't learning these skills they won't be capable of overcoming their difficulties and wont believe they can either."

Dad responded.

Assessing Your Self Esteem 2

Read each statement and tick it if you feel it tends to apply to you

1. When I make mistakes I tend to consider what I could've done to avoid it and think what I've learnt from it.
2. When I look at myself in the mirror, I tend to see someone who is confident and pleased to be me.
3. When I try to solve problems I tend to be able to analyse what caused the situation and able to work (with others if needed) to overcome them.
4. If my views are different from those of others, I am keen and able to argue my point and work with them towards an agreed solution.
5. When I think about the main aims in my life, I tend focus on what is needed to achieve it.
6. When I make a commitment to myself to change and improve I tend to stick to it despite setbacks and difficulties.
7. When I talk to myself, I tend to be very positive, persuading myself I can do it and become re-charged.
8. When other people comment on my actions I tend to think carefully about what they are saying and why, and then decide if I can learn from it.
9. I rarely talk negatively about other people, but try to understand why they think and behave in that way.
10. I rarely tell people what I've achieved; I let others do that for me, though I will inform them of my mistakes and weaknesses.
11. I thoroughly enjoy trying new things, even though I am likely to be poor at it and 'show myself up'.

"Mum, I think you've 'hit the nail on the head' there. I don't really have the skills we need to succeed and I'm not surprised I have low self esteem. I've spent so much of my life doing what I've always done and avoiding new experiences or challenges. I've not really learnt any new skills. I can't use the computer or the internet. I've not been able to give up smoking or drinking despite the problems they cause, especially Dad's death. I've been lucky to have been a plumber all my adult life, if I weren't I don't know what I'd do."

"That's really honest of you, Dad. I had no idea that you felt like that. I've always thought you coped with everything apart from me and my behaviour." Stacey replied emotionally.

"I've never talked about my feelings or concerns, that's why when we talked about the skills we need to succeed the other night it hit me so hard. I realised that I had contributed so much to your problems because of what I haven't done, that's why we've got to have these forums from now on." Dad replied.

Nan tried to consol him by saying.

"Your dad never talked about his feelings or concerns either, Steve. Men didn't do that sort of thing; they just 'bottled it all up'. They weren't brought up in that way, we didn't know anything about those skills or how important they are. You had loads of problems when you were a teenager, not as bad as Stacey's, I admit, but you've never been able to talk about your problems, even after your dad died. He smoked and drunk too much and you're just doing the same."

Dad was so 'full of emotion' that he just about managed to say.

"I'm hoping that the problems Stacey's had and how she's trying to change will help me and hopefully I can help prevent the same thing happen to Suzi".

"Perhaps you could start by giving up smoking like Stacey has. It did kill your dad, Steve. Why did you start?" Nan asked.

"I think I can answer that, Nan." Stacey answered. "It seems that the only reason that people start smoking is because they lack the essential skills, especially self-awareness, managing feelings, motivation and social skills. There appears to be absolutely no positives in taking up smoking but 25% of 15 and 16 year olds smoke. It now seems obvious that it is because they have low self esteem and start to copy others, to feel they are accepted or to try to impress others. That's why I started and I bet that's why Dad started."

"Yep, that's exactly it, but until now I've not been able to give up, probably because I've never developed my skills enough in managing my feelings or motivation." Dad replied.

Stacey then carried on.

"We've got another poster that you might all find interesting, it follows on from the poster you showed us yesterday about parenting. 'AN ENCOURAGED CHILD HAS NO NEED TO MISBEHAVE'

this is the key part to 'positive parenting' which are on the TV programmes and it explains the best way to treat children is to use encouragement and try to avoid being negative by keep telling them off and punishing them. It seems that developing children in this positive way helps to promote good self esteem. "The most important part is to develop their children's cognitive and self-awareness skills by consistently modelling and explaining what they should be doing and why, so that the children understand and learn to manage their emotions. Here is a set of suggestions that you might interest you"

1.How to <u>increase</u> conflict and create problems

- Threaten the child
- View the conflict as a contest
- Handle in front of an audience
- Use threatening gestures and body language
- Give the child no room for manoeuvre
- Raise your voice and sound angry
- Deliver unrealistic ultimatums that cannot be implemented

2.How to <u>reduce</u> conflict and problems

- Label the behaviour not the child
- Avoid threatening gestures and body language
- Give the child a choice, but not an ultimatum
- Avoid dealing with the conflict in front of an audience
- Stay calm (at least on the outside) but don't try to soothe the child as this can make them even more angry
- Give the child time to comply
- Explain clearly what you want
- Show empathy
- Use humour to defuse the situation

Dad studied the poster carefully and then commented.

"If I think about the 8 skills you need to succeed and self esteem, I can see how the second part can help to develop the skills and self esteem" "Unfortunately, I think I tended to use the first part most of the time".

"You weren't alone in that, Steve. I reckon I did as well" Said Mum.

"And me." Said Gran. "But I'd never heard of self esteem, positive parenting or the skills we need to succeed in those days, so how could we know the harm we were doing."

"Exactly right, Sarah" Agreed Nan. "But how many parents know about it now, do you reckon?"

"Hardly any, I suspect. So no wonder so many young people have low self esteem and huge problems." Sheila replied.

"I expect it contributes to the large numbers who suffer from depression, commit self harm and suicide." Stacey added.

"There have been lots on the news about kids committing suicide and having mental health problems. How big a problem is it?" Nan asked.

"I don't know, perhaps me and Suzi can try to find out for tomorrow's forum." Stacey suggested.

"Good idea, Stace." Suzi added

"Yes, please." Added Dad and the others all nodded in agreement.

Chapter 17
Depression, Mental Health, Self Harm and Suicide

"Last week when I attempted suicide, Suze, I thought I was very unusual and I didn't fit in. Now I've found these statistics and news articles, I've realised I'm almost normal for a young person these days. I can't believe how many suffer from depression, have mental health problems, commit self harm and suicide; I'm not unusual at all?" Stacey remarked.

Stacey and Suzi had again begun the next day enthusiastically researching the topic for that day's forum. Both were in their usual positions, Stacey at the computer, Suzi lying on the floor cutting, pasting, drawing and writing to create posters.

"This is going to shock Nan, Gran, Dad and Mum. I don't think they'll have any idea how serious these problems are. I think this could help them understand your problems a lot more, sis." Suzi commented.

"Well I've certainly learnt a lot already, but I desperately want to know more now. What I'm beginning to wonder is why all young people don't become like me, how do any of them become successful, and how do any of them learn the 8 essential skills. I haven't got time to research that now but I'm going to." Stacey said determinedly.

"Stace, I can't believe how much you've changed in the last week. You're like a completely different person. You seem so enthusiastic about all this, especially wanting to learn more. And I can't believe how much I've enjoyed it, even though I'm learning all the time. It's as though learning has suddenly become a great pleasure for us." Suzi remarked.

"I know, Suze. I suppose I just needed the motivation to start to change, the 'buzz' is like being on drugs, but much better and healthier with no hangover or drawback. I feel like I'm on a high all the time, I can't wait to get up each day. It seems the more I learn, the more I want to learn and the buzz I get from helping you, Dad, Mum, Nan and Gran is brilliant. It's the best feeling I've ever had, much better than sex!" Stacey said growing more excited by the minute.

"Whoa, too much information, well at least for the moment anyway, Sis. Though I must admit I would like to know a bit more about your involvement with drink, drugs and sex at some stage, but not just now. I think we've got enough to be getting on with here already." Suzi replied.

"Yeah, you're probably right, Suze. But I do desperately want to research and learn about 'relationships' and I will try to help warn you about the problems I've had over the years. Perhaps in the future we'll focus on this. Anyway, let's get on with these articles and posters. I reckon they will be very shocked by all of this." Stacey responded.

"We've got some very interesting posters today, for you" said Suzi as she, Stacey, Nan, Gran, Dad and Mum sat down in the front room in preparation for the family forum.

"The first one is an article from the 'Mental Health Foundation' on Self Harm. Do any of you know anyone who has self harmed, apart from me?" Stacey asked.

They all nodded to express that they didn't.

"Did you self harm, Stacey? I didn't know you cut yourself." Sheila, her mum asked.

"Self harm is not just about cutting yourself, Mum. "Have a look at this." Stacey replied.

Stacey gave out a sheet to her Mum and Dad, and another one to Nan and Gran. All four had expressions that showed disbelief.

The truth about self-harm from the Mental Health Foundation.

The phrase 'self-harm' is used to describe a range of things that people do to themselves in a deliberate and usually hidden way. It can involve, cutting, burning, scalding, banging or scratching one's own body, breaking bones, hair pulling, swallowing poisonous substances or objects.

Research shows that **1 in 15 young people in Britain have harmed themselves.** Another way of looking at it is that there are probably two young people in every secondary school classroom who have done it at some time. This means it's a very common problem.

Most young people who harm themselves are aged 11-25.

The age at which most people start is 12, but some as young as 7 have been known to do it.

As one young person put it, many people self-harm to 'get out the hurt, anger and pain' caused by pressures in their lives. They harm themselves because they don't know what else to do and because they don't have, or don't feel they have, any other options.

For some young people, self-harm gives temporary relief and a sense of control over their lives. But it brings its own very serious problems.

Nan spoke first.

"This is incredible, I had no idea that it was this bad. Two in every secondary school classroom is a frightening statistic."

Gran then commented.

"It starts as young as 7, amazes me. I watched a TV programme the other day that was about an 8 year old anorexic, and I suppose this is reflecting a similar problem."

"An 8 year old anorexic? That sounds interesting as well." Stacey said and was clearly keen to add this to her research.

"It says 'self-harm gives temporary relief and a sense of control over their lives', so I suppose there are similarities, to anorexia. But how can these kids feel so bad about themselves?" Dad asked.
"It must be related to their low self esteem, the stuff we looked at yesterday. But what causes them to feel that low?" Nan asked.
"We've got some more for you to look at." Suzi remarked.
Stacey got out another sheet from the folder and showed it to them.

A million children now suffer from mental health problems

More than a million children have mental health problems, a doubling of the number in a generation, devastating research reveals an epidemic of disorders ranging from depression, anxiety and anorexia to violent delinquency has struck **one in ten youngsters.**

The children's charity, NCH, called for urgent action to prevent mental health problems wrecking the prospects of a generation.

"One in ten suffering from diagnosed mental health problems. How many go undiagnosed?" Nan asked.
"This is dreadful." Mum commented. "This is like 'epidemic proportions' it's almost as though it's normal for them to be depressed, why is that?"
"Yeah, Stacey, you used to feel like that, do you know why." Dad asked.
"Not really, Dad. I know I have very poor development of the essential skills and that contributed to my very low self esteem. But I don't really know why I felt that bad, though I'm going to try to find out. This next one is probably even worse."
Stacey then gave out two more sheets.

Suicide is the most common cause of death in men aged under 35

(Men's Health Forum, 2002)

Teen male suicides hit 'crisis' levels

The psychiatrist, who carried out the research, says the statistics under-estimate the true extent of the problem because coroners prefer to classify unexplained deaths as "undetermined" or "accidental" if there is any doubt.

"It is something of a crisis for young males.

"It is always a mistake to look for one single cause, but it is probably a crisis of confidence among these young people.

There are many, many more suicides in the 'undetermined deaths' category who are suicides, but aren't labelled because coroners are more reluctant to give a verdict of suicide."

Nineteen Young Suicides In Bridgend

In the last 12 months, 19 young people under the age of 27, many of them in their teens, have committed suicide in and around the South Wales town of Bridgend. The latest death is the 34th since 2006.

Officially, an inquest into five of the deaths, held on March 19, said that the deaths were not related.

A 24-year-old man from Maesteg whose death was investigated at the inquest, was described as "happy go lucky," with no overt signs of depression.

A relative told the press.

"We just don't know what is going on in Bridgend. Kelly and Nathaniel were both brilliant kids with good futures ahead of them. We would never have thought in a million years that they were capable of anything like this.

None of this makes sense."

Warning over youth mental health

Young unemployed adults need more help to deal with mental health problems, the Prince's Trust charity has warned.

One in 10 youngsters questioned in a survey disagreed that "life was really worth living".

Those not in work or education were less likely to be happy. Polling company YouGov questioned 2,004 people aged 16-25 online in October. Paul Brow, of the Prince's Trust, said the study showed there were thousands of young people who "desperately" needed support. He added: "Often young people who feel they have reached rock bottom don't know where to turn for help."

Of those questioned, 29% said they are less happy now than they were as a child and one in five said they felt like crying "often" or "always".

Almost half (47%) said they were regularly stressed.

"I remember the news article about the 'Bridgend Suicides', they thought there was some internet connection between them, but couldn't find anything. Why do so many men, in particular, want to commit suicide?" Gran asked.

"Because they don't talk about their feelings and concerns, they let them build up until they can't cope anymore. That's what we touched upon the other day. I know that's what I've been doing and I'm determined to change that." Dad answered with a great deal of confidence and emotion. "Stacey, you said you're going to research what made you get so depressed, I'm very keen to find out the answer to this one as well".

"It says in the article 'Kelly and Nathaniel were both brilliant kids with good futures ahead of them. We would never have thought in a million years that they were capable of anything like this'. I realised you were struggling Stacey, and I suppose your suicide attempt was not a huge surprise, but these parents must be devastated to suddenly find this happening to their kids." Mum remarked.

"If people don't talk to each other about how they feel and what is worrying them, how will they know what's causing there problems and how they can solve them." Nan replied. "We've discovered over the last few days that people don't talk and listen to each other anymore. The kids can't develop the skills they need to succeed and go from one problem to another, not learning anything until they get to a point that they give up trying, or self-destruct, or worse still 'kill each other'."

Dad then commented on this.

"You're talking about these gangs, stabbing and shooting each other. I suppose those kids just don't care about themselves or anybody else, just like the kids in these articles".

"Why do they have so little respect for themselves or others?" Mum asked.

Stacey was keen to reply.

"They've not developed those skills, Mum, remember. I've discovered lots of stuff on this. Apparently almost 25% of students drop out of university because they can't cope with managing their lives as a result of not having these skills. Being good at exams doesn't seem to have much to do with being happy. Young people don't seem to have much help in trying to improve the skills they need to succeed or on their happiness or well being, just on being academically good."

"We just keep coming back to the importance of developing those skills every time, don't we?" Dad commented.

"This is almost unbelievable, how can we let our kids grow up in this way."

Nan said and was clearly very upset.

"But, how many people know the harm we are causing our kids, Nan?" Stacey asked. "Remember we've only just realised what's been happening, how serious the problem is and why it's occurring."

"You're absolutely right, Stacey. Until these last few days, I had no idea of what a poor parent I've been and how much I've contributed to your problems." Dad said and again became very emotional.

Stacey replied passionately.

"Dad, you must stop beating yourself up about this. You've got to come to terms with the fact that you did what you thought was best, but now you know different. The parents of the kids who have mental health problems, self harm, and commit suicide won't know that. Worse still, parents of the babies or young children who will become victims like these don't know either. What we've got to do, is to do what we can to learn and change, so that Suzi doesn't become one of these statistics and we can help others in the future. We can't turn back the clock, but we can be different in the future."

Suzi started to clap and they all joined in.

"Well said Stacey, you are so right. We must look forward and learn from the past, not keep moaning about it." Dad said and got up and gave Stacey a huge hug. "So what's the topic for tomorrow then?"

"I want to know why teenagers have such low self esteem and get so depressed and do these stupid things." Said Suzi.

"OK, since you are the first person we need to help and prevent it happening to, we'd better focus on that" Stacey said with tears in her eyes at the emotion of the occasion.

Later that night as Stacey and Suzi went to bed; Stacey sat on the side of Suzi's bed and said to her.

"I think this has been my best day ever. I really enjoyed being able to help Nan, Gran, Mum and Dad. On the first night, Arthur showed me a version of Stacey that got such a huge buzz from activities that I've never been able to relate to. I can now understand why she felt like that. It's given me an insight into how some teenagers avoid all the problems that I've experienced and what we were discussing today. What we need to find out is what causes so many teenagers to have such low self esteem, be depressed, and commit self harm and suicide. And try to discover how some teenagers can overcome these difficulties and become successful, so I can help you."

"Not an easy task, Sis, but you've done so much in such a short space of time, who knows" Suzi replied.

Chapter 18
Locus of Control and Mindsets

"This has gone even better than I could possibly have hoped"
Stacey recognised that voice instantly and sat up in bed straightaway.

"Arthur, what did you say?" she said.

Arthur explained.

"When I planned this project, I never thought that you would respond so well, so quickly. You've done incredibly well so far. I've returned to help you with your burning question, 'how I can help Suzi to become a successful teenager', rather than like you were".

Stacey then responded.

"Good, I really need to understand why I and so many teenagers have so many serious problems and how they can be avoided."

"Well you now seem very aware that the key to success is having the 8 skills you need to succeed being well developed. When I showed you the life of the Stacey you could've been, I pointed out that the only difference between you and her was that by the age of 11 she did have these skills well developed and you did not. This is true for virtually all teenagers, they need to have these skills well developed as they begin their teenage years since their brains and bodies undergo such change and problems that without these skills their chances of coping are minimal." Arthur explained.

"What do you mean by 'their brains and bodies undergo such change and problems'" asked Stacey.

Arthur pointed to the bedroom wall and a video of a model of the human brain appeared with lights flashing to highlight key parts and the movement of signals through it.

"I shall begin by attempting to explain a little about how our brain works and develops our learning. I would like you to research this topic on your computer, and you will find that there have been a number of recent discoveries on how the human brain works and how they cause learning. There are now a number of ways of observing the brain in action leading to a number of key discoveries. When a child's brain develops, it goes through several key periods, basically stages of development, in which the brain requires certain inputs or it will not develop."

"The brain's frontal lobe is important in managing and controlling our behaviour and thoughts, and is also crucial to concentration, allowing us to focus and increase our attention span. It seems likely that hyperactivity (ADHD) comes when children can't inhibit or control their movements due to poorly developed concentration. Basically the frontal lobes can't manage the competing thoughts and emotions. It appears that when a child enters puberty the initial burst of hormones may cause dramatic 'disconnection' of the neuron pathways to and from the frontal lobe. This explains why, when they're feeling things they can't control themselves and cannot even explain what it is they're feeling. It seems that teenagers have to go through another period when their pre-frontal lobes are trying to learn to work more efficiently. This frontal lobe is the part of the brain that makes people 'human' and different from the rest of the animals."

Stacey was trying hard to concentrate and interrupted Arthur to check her understanding.

"This is not easy to understand, but does this explain why I and many of my mates seemed to 'go backwards' when I became a teenager. My concentration got worse and I felt restless and uncomfortable in the classroom, lost my confidence and then my interest in studying"

Arthur was clearly pleased with this observation and said.

"Yes, you've got it, those neuron pathways to your frontal lobe were weak to begin with, so with puberty, these hormones easily caused sufficient disruption for you to 'lose it' and your emotional brain took over."

Stacey was also pleased and asked.

"So what we've got to do with Suzi is to spend a lot of time practising and developing these effective learning, cognitive and communication skills before she becomes a teenager and then to keep her motivated to continue with this practice when puberty strikes"

A smiling Arthur responded.

"Absolutely correct, you've got it so far. But I'm not finished yet; there are still a few problems you need to be aware of. Since one of the key roles of the frontal lobe is developing our understanding and interpreting the facial expressions of others, teenagers seem not to be very good at this and will often struggle to detect various expressions on peoples' faces. This meant you began to struggle to communicate with boys, your friends and others very well and frequently seemed to misunderstand their gestures, subtle comments, signs and body language, that they often felt were obvious. This frustration almost certainly contributed towards your quick loss of temper, frequent annoyance and aggression"

Throughout this explanation, video clips of a young Stacey showing these problems throughout her teenage years, illustrated his points.

Stacey seemed to understand and commented.

"This is very helpful. I've struggled to understand why I had so many arguments and problems with other girls and adults. I think I need to unravel my problems with boys a bit more though, can you help me with that, please."

Arthur replied.

"I'll try, but this part is even more complex and you will need to research this much further. You've already learnt a lot about Motivation, Maslow's Hierarchy and Self Esteem, so I'll follow these with a focus on what influenced your self esteem as a teenager. You and your friends put a very high value on being attractive, 'sexy', and having the 'right look and label'. This was because you, like so many teenage girls, were so influenced by television, film and pop stars, media celebrities and fashion. Unfortunately, if a person puts a high value on things that depends a great deal on other people's opinion, it means they don't have much control over it. This is called their 'locus of control', so it means 'their life is not in their own hands'. Your teenage years were controlled by other people's opinions and obviously you became frustrated and upset on many occasions. Teenagers, who repeatedly compare themselves with others, increasingly tend to feel more powerless, frustrated, angry, desperate and particularly depressed."

Stacey commented on this.

"This explains why so many teenagers are depressed so much of the time, and I suppose it will result in mental health problems, self harm and suicide."

Arthur then continued.

"Look into eating disorders, anorexia and obesity, drug abuse, binge drinking, promiscuity, bullying, anti-social and violent behaviour, gambling and even 'retail therapy' will have this poor 'locus of control' relating to it. If people have not developed the 8 skills they need to succeed, their lives become controlled by these external factors and become out of control."

"So what was different about the 'Skilful Stacey' you showed me." Stacey asked.

Arthur answered her promptly.

"When 'Skilful Stacey' began secondary school, she became very interested in trying new experiences and developing new skills, things over which she had control. You've started to experience this in the last week; you've experienced the joy of learning and helping others. You've switched your locus of control to things over which you have influence, it's called 'internal locus of control'. The successful teenagers and people in general have a 'growth mindset', another term to research that means they value and enjoy learning and the get their joy, happiness and well being from skills they've learnt and things they've achieved."

142

Again video clips of the 'Skilful Stacey' illustrated his point.

Stacey seemed very pleased and responded.

"I can understand that now. I've experienced this feeling now and I can appreciate why people would prefer this to worrying about image and appearance all the time. So it is important to get Suzi to experience this as soon as possible and try to help her keep values that means she is in control, an 'internal locus of control' I think you called it."

"You've got it, well done". Arthur commented.

"But how do boys and sex fit into this?" Stacey asked.

Arthur answered her.

"This is a major example of the problems of 'external locus of control'. Quite simply, if you recall from 'Maslows Hierarchy' the major motivation priorities for most teenagers will be 'sense of belonging and self esteem'. For you and many teenagers you desperately wanted to have boys being attracted to you because it made you feel important and attached".

Several scenes of Stacey wearing low cut tops and short skirts chatting up boys and fighting girls emphasised his point.

"Unfortunately, this was too superficial and you relied on using sex and advertising sex to attract them. Sadly this meant that the boys weren't actually attracted to you as a person but simply to what they could get from you, so it actually lowered your self esteem and made you feel used and no sense of belonging."

Stacey could obviously appreciate this and said.

"This is very true, because I gained such a reputation as a slag or slapper that my self esteem hit rock bottom, and was a major factor in my suicide attempt."

"Do you feel more confident now that you understand why you and teenagers have so many serious problems and what is needed to reduce Suzi's chances of experiencing them?" Arthur asked.

"I do and when I've done my research and explained it to the others I think I'll be even clearer, thank you," Stacey answered.

"I'm sure it will, you are learning very well, all the best" Arthur said and raised his arm and as usual, disappeared into the bright white light.

Chapter 19
Trying To Understand Teenagers

"Are you awake, Stace" Suzi was gently tapping on the bedroom door.

"Yeah, Suze, I am, come in." Stacey woke quickly and replied straightaway.

"He's been again. Arthur visited me last night, he was brilliant. I think I know why I was the 'teenager from hell' and why so many have problems."

Suzi sat down on the side of Stacey's bed as Stacey sat upright in bed and lent over to write on her pad.

"What you going to write down this time, Stace?" Suzi asked.

"I've got loads, I'm not sure if I can remember them all though. The first one is 'Locus of Control'.

"What! What the devil's that?" Suzi asked.

"I'll explain later." Stacey commented. "I've got much more to write. 'Mindsets', 'Neuron Pathways', 'Frontal Lobe', 'Teenage Sex', 'Anorexia', 'Obesity', Drugs', 'Binge Drinking', 'Bullying', 'Retail Therapy'. I think that's about it. I can't think of any more."

"You've written a lot there, sis. We won't get all that sorted by dinner will we?" Suzi questioned.

"No, there are lots to research and loads to explain. We'll start with 'How the Brain causes Learning', 'Neuron Pathways', 'Frontal Lobe' and 'Locus of Control'." Stacey suggested.

"Well I don't understand any of them, so you've got a tough task today." Suzi added.

"Fortunately, Arthur explained them so well; I think I'll be OK." Stacey replied. "But we've got lots to do so we'd better get going."

The girls sprang up, showered, dressed, had breakfast and began their 'studying', Stacey at the computer, Suzi on the floor, as usual. Both girls were amazed that within what seemed like minutes, it was time for dinner and the family forum.

"What's the topic for today's forum Stacey?" Nan asked displaying obvious enthusiasm, as they were walking into the front room after finishing dinner.

"Understanding Teenage Problems', Nan." Stacey replied.

"That's something I definitely need to learn." Dad responded.

"We all do." Mum added.

Stacey waited for everone to be ready and then began.

"We're going to start with a science lesson, biology. We're going to study the human brain and how it causes us to learn. We learn because connections between parts of the brain are formed, they are called 'Neuron Pathways'. Our brain receives and records information with the thickening of these pathways, so that the more this happens the thicker the pathway. This means we have learnt skills because we've repeated the activity so many times, that the neuron pathways have become very thick and so the messages can easily flow through the brain. If the activity is not repeated enough the pathway is too thin and information is not passed very well so we don't learn and can't do it. The phrase 'Use it or lose it' is often applied to illustrate this learning in the brain."

Suzi interrupted with this suggestion.

"So we learn by making links between parts of the brain, like having a strip of sellotape joining them together. The more strips of sellotape the stronger the link, the stronger the learning."

"That's it. What an excellent way of explaining it, Suze. Well done." Stacey replied and Suzi visibly beamed with pride.

"Yes that makes sense, I can understand that." Said Dad and the others agreed.

"This poster should help to explain why teenagers have particular problems." Stacey said as she handed out a sheet to everyone.

TRYING TO EXPLAIN WHY TEENAGERS THINK AND BEHAVE SO DIFFERENTLY

The bizarre behaviour of teenagers appears to be more explained by their neurobiology (brain development) rather than their hormones.

It's been thought for a long time that brain development was set at a fairly early age and by the time children became teenagers the development of their brain was thought to be largely finished. Scientists have discovered the brain continues to change into the early 20's with the frontal lobes, responsible for reasoning and problem solving, developing last. This means that the part of the brain largely responsible for decision making doesn't fully develop until young adulthood.

In calm situations, teenagers can think rationally almost as well as adults, but stress can hijack 'thinking and decision-making'.

The frontal lobes tend to help manage or control the emotional part of the brain, reducing the desire for thrills and risk – taking, common characteristics of teenage behaviour.

Scientists think the brain develops early in life through a "use-it-or-lose-it:" principle causing the neural connections, or synapses, that get exercised to be retained and thickened, while those that don't get used are lost.

This process in the frontal part of the brain peaks at about age 11 or 12 about the same time as puberty. After that peak, the neural pathways and connections start to get thinner as the excess connections are eliminated or pruned. This means that although teenagers are capable of learning a lot, the parts of their brains related to emotions and decision-making are still undergoing rewiring, and are particularly vulnerable to high risk and emotional behaviour. Puberty and the early adult years is a particularly critical time for the brain wiring. Basically it is probably unfair to expect teenagers to have adult levels of organizational skills or decision-making until their brains are completely finished being developed.

Stacey waited for everyone to study it and then continued.

"This means unless there are very strong connections between the frontal lobe and the rest of the brain, the sellotape is very thick as you describe it Suze, when they start to thin during puberty the frontal lobe will not have much effect on the rest of the brain. Therefore, teenagers are likely to be poor at organising, reasoning and problem solving, decision making and recognising emotions. The effects of alcohol are very similar though temporary, alcohol reduces the control the frontal lobe exerts on our emotional brain and we do stupid things because of our emotional brain takes over."

Locus of Control

Locus of control refers to a person's belief about what causes the good or bad results in his or her life, either in general or in a specific area such as health or academics.

internal (meaning the person believes that they control their life) or

external (meaning they believe that their environment, some higher power, or other people control their decisions and their life).

For example, college students with a ***strong internal locus of control*** may believe that their grades were achieved through their own abilities and efforts, whereas those with a ***strong external locus of control*** may believe that their grades are the result of good or bad luck, or to a professor who designs bad tests or grades capriciously; hence, they are less likely to expect that their own efforts will result in success and are therefore less likely to work hard for high grades.

Due to their locating control outside themselves, externals tend to feel they have less control over their fate. People with an external locus of control tend to be more stressed and prone to <u>clinical depression</u>

Nan then commented.

"This makes so much sense and explains a lot of what we were considering yesterday, Clearly, these poor young people are being controlled by their emotions and can easily become depressed or have mental health problems, commit self harm or suicide."

Stacey then responded.

"I've got much more information yet, Nan that helps explain those problems. These two posters also help to explain what happens to us, they are called 'Locus of Control' and 'Mindsets'. These both describe ways that we think and make decisions. Probably because of their poor development of the essential skills many teenagers seem to have external locus of control and fixed mindsets, which helps to explain their problems."

Mindsets

Fixed Mindset - people believe that their talents and abilities are fixed traits. They have a certain amount and that's that; nothing can be done to change it. When people adopt the fixed mindset, it can limit their success. They become over-concerned with proving their talents and abilities, hiding deficiencies, and reacting defensively to mistakes or setbacks-because deficiencies and mistakes imply a (permanent) lack of talent or ability. People in this mindset will actually pass up important opportunities to learn and grow if there is a risk of unmasking weaknesses.

Growth mindset - people believe that their talents and abilities can be developed through passion, education, and persistence. For them, it's not about looking smart or grooming their image. It's about a commitment to learning--taking informed risks and learning from the results, surrounding yourself with people who will challenge you to grow, looking frankly at your deficiencies and seeking to remedy them. Most great business leaders have had this mindset, because building and maintaining excellent organizations in the face of constant change requires it.

"What causes these young people to have external locus of control and fixed mindsets?" Asked Dad, who was clearly fascinated by this information?

"I think I can answer that." Nan replied. "It is the same as 'developing the skills we need to succeed', that we discussed the other day. We used to develop it by doing the activities we used to do when I was young. We did lots of activities with our family and friends, where we were trying lots of new things, sometimes feeling success, sometimes failure and then talking and thinking about it afterwards. We used to grow up being given responsibility and believing we were responsible for our destiny, and told to 'stop whingeing and get on with it'."

"Well put, Nan." Stacey commented. "I've found this news article which calls kids today 'Cotton wool kids' because they are not given responsibility and take so few risks, it gives a lot of support to 'The Incapable Generation' one we looked at the other day.

Gran then remarked.

"Although I think I understand why the teenage brain is likely to have problems and how the 'Locus of control and Mindsets' are developed, I still don't understand why these teenagers do the stupid and unpleasant things that they do, like self harm, suicide, kill each other, take drugs, have eating disorders etc."

"That's a good point, Gran" replied Stacey. "I will try to explain that, by looking at myself as a typical teenager. Last week I thought I was very unusual and that bad things only seemed to happen to me, and I was wondering 'what have I done to deserve this' all the time. Now I know that I was just like most teenagers and bad things are happening to most of us, most of the time because of the stupid decisions we make. I now think I understand why I made those stupid decisions, which is probably what you want to know."

"Yes please, very much so." Dad said promptly.

"If you remember the diagram of 'Maslow's Hierarchy' which explains what motivates us, the key ones for me as a typical teenager are 'Sense of belonging and self esteem'. What

Raising Cotton Wool Kids

- In 1971 eight out of ten children aged seven or eight years went to school on their own. By 1990 this figure had dropped to less than one in ten.
- In 1971 the average seven-year-old made solo trips to their friends or the shops. By 1990 that freedom was with held until the age of ten.
- Children today spend about four times as much time being looked after by their parents as children did in 1975.
- With the introduction of extended school hours, children may spend more time at school, where in many cases they have less unstructured free time than in the past.
- What has happened in the last 30 years or so?
- The risk of abduction remains tiny. In Britain, there are now half as many children killed every year in road accidents as there were in 1922 - despite a more than 25-fold increase in traffic.
- In 1970, 80% of primary school-age children made the journey from home to school on their own. It was what you did.
- Today the figure is under 9%. Escorting children is now the norm - often in the back of a 4x4.
- We are rearing our children in captivity - their habitat shrinking almost daily.
- In 1970 the average nine-year-old girl would have been free to wander 840 metres from her front door. By 1997 it was 280 metres.
- Now the limit appears to have come down to the front doorstep.

motivated me every day was 'wanting to be accepted by my mates' and if my mates, boys in particular, liked me I felt I was the business."

"Everything I did was to impress or be accepted by them. The things they thought was important became what I thought were important, what they did, I did. I know now that my insecurity, low self esteem at age 11, meant I was desperate to find things that my mates would appreciate and with such poorly developed skills I was struggling to find things that could do this. So I played the fool, became a rebel, did extremely risky and anti-social activities to try to impress them.

As I became older, I focused more and more on trying to attract boys as a way of feeling I mattered. I spent a vast quantity of time, money and effort on my appearance in an effort to make myself attractive to them and going clubbing to meet them. "

"Virtually all my time and thoughts were focused on trying to impress the boys or making my friends jealous, I had no other particular interests at all. Very quickly, I realised that the possible offer of sex was a huge attraction to boys and as a young teenager I started to explore different ways to use sex to attract them. I dressed very sexily as much as possible, revealing as much flesh as I could, especially my boobs, which I exposed as much as possible and increasingly allowed the boys to fondle them and touch my flesh, this became a huge attraction to them."

"Unfortunately, I had to continue to 'up the stakes', so I began fondling the boys and performing 'hand jobs and oral sex' on them. All these activities, understandably got lots of interest from lots of boys, and the girls became more and more jealous, at least I thought so, therefore I continued with it. In fact, I lost my virginity in my early teens, it seemed essential and natural at the time with so much pressure and expectation on me."

"Having sex made me feel I had 'grown up' and that others were inexperienced and naïve, and were jealous of me. Consequently, I began to have sex regularly with a variety of boys, they became very attracted to me and I felt 'popular'. Some girls and a few boys showed their envy by calling me names but I soon 'sorted them out' and becoming feared by other girls also made me feel important."

"I was keen to try any activities that I felt others were frightened to do, because I felt my mates and particularly the boys would think how 'gutsy' or brave I was, so I 'got slaughtered' regularly, that's often called binge drinking, smoking, trying various drugs, doing all sorts of anti-social and criminal behaviour, like nicking stuff in shops or 'twocing cars', that's taking and driving cars."

"By my mid-teens, I had created such a reputation that there were huge expectations on me from all sorts of people, particularly my mates and boys, so I couldn't back down, otherwise I would 'lose face'. Obviously I had become known as a 'slut, slag or slapper', but there was no turning back at this stage, the slippery slope I was on was much too difficult to climb up. Although I had desperately wanted to 'feel I belonged and have good self esteem', I had actually achieved the complete opposite. The boys only wanted me for sex, the girls hated me and my mates felt they couldn't trust me, quite simply I was getting to the point that I had no 'sense of belonging or self esteem'."

"As I entered my late teens, I began to realise that the chances of me having good friends, getting a good job or most importantly having a good boyfriend was virtually none. I felt all the things that mattered had become impossible to achieve so I became increasingly depressed until I decided there were no good things left in my life and no point carrying on, so I decided to end it by drinking the vodka and taking the pills."

Everyone in the room, including Stacey was crying. Stacey's mum was quickest to hug her, but they all either touched or held her hand, grabbing tissues and wiping their eyes.

"I think we all need a drink after that" Said Mum.

"I'll put the kettle on" Suzi suggested.

Chapter 20
Saving Suzi

"That was so brave and honest of you, Stacey and it has really helped me understand where you were coming from. I really couldn't understand or cope with you, to be honest" Dad commented.

"I must admit that I did at least realise that 'Boys and social life' had become your only interests, but I had no idea how stupid and desperate you had become." Mum said.

"We were interested in boys, of course, when I was a teenager, but it didn't dominate and control our lives like yours". Gran remarked.

"But that's because we had better development of the skills you need to succeed. Stacey has helped us realise how essential they are and what is likely to happen if teenagers don't have them. Which leads us on to the key question, how do we prevent Suzi going down this slippery slope?" Nan asked.

"I'd certainly like to know the answer to that." Suzi responded.

"I think the answer to that lies with a study of the successful teenagers. I've recently had a chance to research one closely and I think I understand what needs to happen." Stacey was, of course referring to the 'Skilful Stacey' that Arthur had shown her.

"OK, Stacey we're 'all ears'". Dad said.

"I have a few posters that might help; the first one contains 2 quotes that I think are helpful. Remember for Suzi to have a chance of succeeding she needs to develop the skills we need to succeed and these quotes refer to the learning of them."

Stacey gave out a sheet to everyone.

> # I'm too busy drowning to learn to swim! –
> # If we don't take time to learn we can't succeed

> # It takes a whole village to raise a child

Stacey allowed them to read them and then explained.

"The first one emphasises the importance of prioritising learning. If anyone is to succeed they must ensure they focus on learning and the second one points out that we must all support Suzi in this learning. If children are to learn the skills they need to succeed, everyone needs to help in the process, not just leave it to parents or teachers. Suzi has already made a good start to learning these skills this week, particularly effective learning, cognitive and self-awareness. She's made this poster for us to remind us of the skills we need to succeed."

They all admired the poster that Suzi had prepared.

Skills We Need To Succeed

Skills To Learn Effectively
In the 21st century life is very complex and continually changing. Only **Successful Learners** will adapt to these new life conditions.

Cognitive skills
If we are to succeed we have to **learn to make good decisions** with long term positive consequences.
Analytical thinking –detect the key information for our decision.
Conceptual thinking-understand and relate this information to overcome our difficulties

Motivation
To learn we must experience setbacks and we need to learn to stay hopeful despite these setbacks so that we become **RESILIENT,** otherwise we avoid attempting to overcome our difficulties

Communication skills
We need to learn to improve our:
• **Concentration** and increase our
• **Attention span** to receive information.
• **Verbal skills** (speaking, listening, reading, writing) and
• **Non-verbal skills** (visual gestures, body language, touch) to understand and convey information

Empathy
We are dependent on others to help us survive, and we need to learn to become sensitive to others emotions, and appreciate others' feelings in order to overcome our difficulties

Managing feelings
We are born unable to control our impulses, to learn how to manage our emotions and 'delay gratification' is essential for our success

Social skills
Our need for attachment with others means we have a desire to be popular, so we need to learn to deal effectively with others. Learning to avoid following other people's poor decisions to become an effective leader.

Self-awareness
Learning to understand our emotions and discover our strengths and weaknesses is vital in both developing self-esteem and success

---

Stacey continued her explanation.

"Hopefully the last few days have given us a clear understanding of how skills are learnt and these ones in particular this next poster is one that Suzi has created to emphasis some of the key points."

(see facing page)

Again they all studied the poster and Nan commented first.

"I suppose there are some major differences to the way things were in my day."

"I can't see anything there that we can't do. What do you reckon, Sheila? Dad asked.

"In fact, I like the idea of it. So much of the television is rubbish and I can record and watch my programmes when it suits me." Mum responded.

Dad was impressed by her observation and said.

"Excellent point, Sheila. I could do the same with my sport and movies, we could set a specific time for the 'Family Forum'."

Developing The Skills We Need To Succeed
The 5 Learning Requirements

MOTIVATION	We are motivated to 'belong and feel attached', so we need people to regularly teach and MODEL THEM for us.
CONCENTRATION (REFLECTION)	Opportunities and time to focus and reflect (think deeply) on our difficulties, experiences and feelings
ENVIRONMENT	Time and environments that allow us to observe, reflect and discuss our difficulties, experiences and
ATTAINABLE TASKS	Tasks involving interaction with people to share difficulties, experiences and feelings FAMILY FORUM, HOUSEWORK JOBS, FAMILY GAMES & CHALLENGES, HOBBIES, SUPERlearning for exam success.
FEELING SUCCESS	Experience the elation in overcoming difficulties, and the importance of encouragement or emotionally healthy constructive criticism (FAMILY FORUM)

Activities For Learning

Good Role Models- We must continually attempt to demonstrate and develop the skills ourselves and apologise when we don't to emphasise the importance of them.

Reflection Time- Time must be planned and set aside to consider what has happened and ensure learning occurs. Diaries used to help with this, refection logs are used now.

Family Forums- These are invaluable, particularly communication, self-awareness, empathy and social skills. Before television they used to occur **daily**, this needs to occur.

Housework Jobs- These develop empathy, managing emotions and motivation, providing a sense of responsibility.

Family Games- Before television these would develop all the skills, complex board or card games are particularly effective.

Hobbies-These provide interests and develop skills.

SUPERlearning- Using this process to achieve exam success can develop effective learning, cognitive and motivation skills.

"This is like trying to step back in time really. Most of this used to happen when I was Suzi's age. I used to keep a diary, I found it very useful." Nan commented.

"But did you have good role models?" Gran asked.

Nan replied. "Some of the time, but the men in my family didn't talk about their emotions and concerns, and I suppose they were bullies, hypocrites and sexist. But most men were like that in those days. Come to think of it, my mother was very sexist as well; she had no career aims and just wanted to be a wife and mother."

"Family forums and playing family games', what's your opinion, Suzi?" Dad asked.

"I like it a lot, especially if Stacey is going to be involved." Suzi said excitedly.

"Of course, I am Suze. I've caused enough problems for this family, the least I can do is try to help." Stacey replied.

"Can I be involved?" Nan asked.

"And me, please?" Gran added.

"Yes, of course, I can't see why not. You can join us when ever you want; I think it will help enormously." Dad responded.

"Well I think we've got 'the village to raise our child' said Dad. "But remember all of you, we've got to do this for many years, 'Success in life is a marathon, not a sprint".

"That's very true Dad. Suzi and I have found another poster that we think Nan and Gran will love." Stacey remarked and displayed the 'Growing Up Learning To Succeed' poster.

They all read it very carefully.

"Absolutely brilliant, and so very true." Nan commented.

"And I agree entirely with that last line." Said Gran.

"The focus in recent years to buy their kids everything, has done so much damage."

Growing Up Learning To Succeed

"That which does not kill us makes us stronger".

Friedrich Nietzsche

Those of us who were kids in the 50's and 60's probably think this was how we learnt the skills needed to succeed. Although we may have had short term pain it helped us achieve long term gain. Daily news articles and reports illustrate young people today are struggling to achieve long term gain and can't cope with setbacks and life in general. Perhaps that's because unlike us we learnt to:

- Accept that much of our food tasted horrible but was natural and didn't make us fat.
- Eat what we were given, because there was no choice.
- Realise that certain foods were treats because they were rare and special
- Copy our family by watching and listening to them instead of being bombarded by electronic shapes and noises.
- Be excited by books when our parents read to us.
- Tolerate pain by learning to crawl, stand, walk, climb, fall down and fight with our brothers and sisters a lot.
- Concentrate by our family playing with us instead of leaving us to watch coloured lights on a screen.
- Enjoy hugging and cuddling because it was how our family showed they cared, and not by being bought stuff.
- Expect to get what we want would only cause our family to laugh, and getting what we needed was much more important.
- Be both good winners and good losers otherwise we didn't get to play games with our family.
- Listen carefully and speak clearly otherwise our family ignored us.

- Look after our money and possessions, otherwise we didn't get any.
- Understand that work is any activity that we didn't want to do but had to and if we didn't help around the house we didn't get any money or possessions.
- Solve problems because we experienced loads and although people gave us clues they wouldn't do it for us.
- Make good decisions because we made lots of bad ones and learnt from the consequences.
- Become confident, because our family wouldn't let us give up.
- Have initiative and be creative because we had no satellite TV, DVDs, computers, video games or internet.
- Organise and plan our lives because we had no mobile phones to allow us to leave everything to last minute and keep changing our minds.
- Be healthy because most us didn't have cars and had to walk everywhere.
- Be honest, as dishonesty was almost a hanging offence to my family.
- Respect ourselves and others because our family continually showed us they cared and considered our thoughts and feelings.
- Be responsible because we trusted to leave home in the morning and play all day, as long as we were back before it got dark, with no one able to reach us.

We had the motivation, environment and opportunities to learn, and had the chance to feel success when we did. It didn't kill most of us and made us strong enough to survive and succeed, perhaps if our children have this chance they may not struggle so much as adults and be unable to cope.

How lucky we were to appear to have so much poverty but actually have so much that matters.

Chapter 21
SUPERlearning To Succeed?

"Stace, Stace, are you up?" Suzi was again gently tapping on Stacey's bedroom door.

"Come on in Suze," Stacey had become used to Suzi waking her in the morning, but unlike the 'old Stacey' she found this very sweet and endearing.

"Did he visit you, Stace? Arthur, did he visit?" Suzi asked.

"No, not this time, Suze." Stacey replied.

"What we going to focus upon today, Stace?" Suzi asked excitedly.

"SUPERlearning keeps cropping up and I would like Nan, Gran, Dad, Mum and you to consider what I need to do ensure my complete recovery, so that my improvement is not 'just a flash in the pan' and I start to become more like the 'Skilful Stacey' that Arthur showed me."

"Well, I'm itching to discover what SUPERlearning is and I think like me, Dad, Mum, Nan and Gran will do all that they can to help you." Suzi commented.

"OK, let's get ready and we'll start as soon as possible" Stacey replied. The girls got up and did just that.

Once again the morning and afternoon seemed to fly by to the girls; they were so engaged in their study and research. Stacey had become very effective at researching on the internet and Suzi was now very skilled at producing posters. The two girls went downstairs with their folder and posters for dinner and the family forum that follows it.

As they were finishing dinner, Dad, said.

"Stacey, I have been amazed at the change in you this week and the family forums have been absolutely brilliant for me, I can't believe how much I've learnt. Yesterday was the best yet; your explanation of your teenage problems and how we could help Suzi was outstanding. I really want to thank you for it. Having helped us so much, there is one thing I'd like to ask. What can we do to help you?"

"Thank you for that and an excellent question, Dad. In fact Suzi and I have tried to prepare stuff to focus on that question." Stacey replied.

"OK, lets all go into the front room then. I'll make the tea and bring it through." Mum said.

They all got up and went to the front room.

Stacey began to speak as Suzi showed them the SUPERlearning poster she had prepared.

S	<u>S</u>TART WITH THE END IN MIND – you must START by knowing clearly what success actually means – being clear what you are actually aiming to achieve (your final destination).
U	<u>U</u>NDERSTAND HOW TO ACHIEVE SUCCESS – you must be sure you are clear on the difficulties preventing success and how you can overcome them.
P	<u>P</u>ERSONALISE YOUR LEARNING – you need to know how you learn most effectively so you can apply it to overcome these difficulties.
E	<u>E</u>VALUATE YOUR LEARNING – you must keep checking that you are making progress and 'feel success', so you avoid wasting time and effort and don't give up!
R	<u>R</u>ESOURCES FOR YOUR EFFECTIVE LEARNING – you need to use the most suitable resources for you (including the right environment and tasks) that helps you overcome these difficulties effectively.

learning

"We are going to start by showing you another poster that Suzi has made. As you can see the letters of 'SUPER', refers to the 5 key steps needed for effective learning. Basically it is a 'Learning Journey' and the key steps outline how to get to your destination effectively." "When you start this journey, as with any, you need to be clear on where you aim to go, so basically it is essential to be clear on what you wish to learn. For us, we now know that the destination of the 'Learning Journey' for children is to learn the 8 skills we need to succeed, and so when children are born their needs to be a continual focus on learning them."

"That makes sense; I think we've all understood that now." Dad commented.

Stacey continued.

"That's why the next step is to 'Understand how this learning occurs'. Over the last few days we've looked at the '5 Learning Requirements', 'The Learning Pyramid', 'How we learn skills' and 'How the brain learns' to help with this understanding. Again using the journey comparison, this is being aware of all the various ways that you could travel to your destination."

"We've certainly discovered a vast amount about how we learn this week; I wish I knew that years and years ago." Nan commented.

Stacey continued her explanation.

"Personalising the learning is about making the most effective decisions for you, personally. We are all individuals and we must not allow others to determine how we should learn because it may not be the most effective for us. In the same way if we allow others to determine how we should travel, they need to know if we can ride a bike, drive, prepared to fly, know how to catch buses or trains etc. We must make these decisions. A simple glance at 'The Learning Pyramid' will show that for many years, most students have been expected to learn in very ineffective ways and understandably become 'underachievers' like me."

"And me" said Mum.

"And me" said Dad.

"And me" said Nan.

"And me" said Gran.

Stacey carried on.

"You will recall from 'The Five Learning Requirements' that we must have 'attainable tasks and feel success' to learn, and 'Evaluating what we have learnt' continually is essential. In fact, we must continually assess what we're doing and learning. Can you imagine trying to learn to kick a football and not observing were it goes, of course not, and using the 'journey of learning' comparison, we need to know where we are on any journey otherwise we get lost. This means we must ensure we are able to reflect on what we've learnt to know where we are to go next, apparently the term in the internet for this is 'Assessment for Learning'."

Dad interrupted with this remark.

"Using the 'Learning Journey' comparison makes this obvious, and yet we usually seem to avoid assessing ourselves or having tests, yet if we were learning to drive we would always have to do this whenever we're at the wheel. It's so obvious when you really think about it!"

Stacey then continued.

"The final step is 'Resources for effective learning' should again be obvious, since we wouldn't try to learn to drive in an unsuitable car with poor clutch, gears, brakes etc. and this applies to anything we wish to learn. If we try to learn using ineffective resources we are unlikely to succeed and yet this occurs frequently, especially in schools. Again using the 'Learning Journey' comparison, our journey will stop if we are not using an efficient vehicle, map, signposts etc."

Nan commented this time.

"Again this is so true, yet rarely considered and applied. No wonder I've found learning to be such hard work all my life."

Stacey replied to this comment.

"That is an important comment, Nan. Most people seem to consider learning to be 'work' and yet Suzi and I have learnt loads this last week and not found any of it to be hard work. In fact, we've thoroughly enjoyed learning, it's been huge fun hasn't it, Suze?"

Suzi continued enthusiastically.

"SUPERlearning is perfect for exam preparation. Stacey and I are going to apply this to learning for exams from now on, we're going to get lots of exam papers and mark schemes, make lots of posters like we've been doing recently, do lots of questions like quizzes, Stacey's says she's going to be the 'Quiz Mistress', like Ann Robinson, but a nice one. She's going to use 'Quizcards' that we're going to prepare from the exam papers and mark schemes and use questions on videos (videostudy) from BBC Bitesize."

"Sounds like a lot of fun." Gran commented.

"I think it's brilliant." Dad said." I wish I'd done this when I was at school."

"So do I, Dad" Stacey responded instantly." But it's never too late to learn, and I aim to use this from now on."

"So what are you going to do then Stacey?" Nan asked.

"Right, well I've actually used SUPERlearning to prepare for my future. The first thing I needed to consider was 'Start with the end in mind' and this became very easy to answer because I clearly need to learn the skills we need to succeed. Hopefully, it is now obvious that until I have those skills I am unlikely to be successful. From then, using SUPERlearning, it became simple to decide what I needed to do to succeed, unfortunately I don't think it will be simple to achieve, but I'm determined to try." Stacey explained.

"Stacey, If the last week is anything to go by, you may just be able to do it." Dad commented.

"That's very kind of you, Dad. But it has only been a few days and I've not even left the house, yet. I am very aware of how difficult it is going to be so I have some posters here that have some quotes on them to keep me motivated." Stacey responded.

"We could display them around the house to inspire and motivate all of us" Mum suggested.

"Excellent idea, Mum. I certainly need all the help I can get to learn and change, starting with giving up smoking." Dad responded.

Applause spontaneously occurred at his comment.

> # WORK is doing something you don't want to do -
>
> # but have to -
>
> # If you learn to enjoy what you have to do -
>
> # You'll never have to work again!

Here are the posters, what do you think/" Suzi asked.

"Excellent, this is so true. Most of my hobbies are activities that other people call work" Nan remarked.

> # When should a child stop taking from their parents and start giving?

"This is a very interesting question, what's so important about this then, Stacey" Gran asked.

Stacey answered her immediately.

"I'm nearly 20 years old, Gran, and throughout that time my parents have spent a fortune on me, given me huge quantity of their time and vast amounts of support, and all I've done is give them loads of grief and problems in return. At what stage do children start to spend vast quantities of their time, money and support for their parents? I think I should've started doing this many, years ago but instead I'm still dependent on them."

Gran was delighted with the answer and responded.

"That's why I asked, Stacey. I went out to work in 1958 at the age of 14 and had to pay rent and board to my parents from what I earned, I didn't complain, it made sense to me."

Stacey again responded.

"It makes sense to me as well, Gran. I think it has been wrong for me not to have supported myself and helped my parents for all these years, that's why I hope it will inspire and motivate me and Suzi in the future not to take our parents for granted and appreciate them as often as possible."

Both Stacey's parents had tears in their eyes.

"This is why, Suzi and I have produced the next one, we feel taking all of you and our lives for granted is a major obstacle to success."

For Success
It Helps To Expect Nothing &
Appreciate Everything

"But our favourite is this final one, because I've now realised that success will only occur when we learn and learning the skills we need to succeed is central to this".

Give a man a fish and
you feed him for a day.
Teach him how to fish and
you feed him for a lifetime.
Teach him how to learn to
overcome his difficulties and
you give him success for life

They all stared at it for a while and finally Dad commented, despite the lump in his throat.

"I think in the last week we've all discovered the wisdom in this. The importance of the first of the skills we need to succeed, 'Effective Learning' has become clear to all of us".

"What we've learnt from you and Suzi in the last few days has been incredible" Nan commented

"I now know I've got to focus on learning, from now on." Mum commented.

"And I certainly have." Said Suzi.

"This is certainly an outstanding poster, but what exactly are you hoping to do from now on?" Mum asked.

Stacey replied.

"Throughout my teenage years, my main motivation and only real interests have been boys and socializing, not any more. I have realised that my motivation has been completely flawed and I have found such great pleasure and happiness this week from learning, helping people and interacting with my family, the people I can be open, honest and fair with and I intend for this to continue in the future."

"I have already arranged to help Suzi with SUPERlearning to help her with exam success, but we have agreed from now on I will try to become not just an older sister but an excellent role model and mentor for her, again continuing what has happened this week. Part of this positive role modelling is I intend to resume studying, try to get into college or evening classes if possible, and use SUPERlearning for exam success for myself. But I am also going to try to get a job to begin paying off my debts and repay my parents as much as I can. Clearly, as you can see I no longer intend to smoke, and this will apply to binge drinking and unhealthy eating, clubbing, boys, sex, drugs, gambling, fashion, excessive watching of television or excessively using the internet (facebook) and mobile phone for communicating with people. But excessively researching and discussing important issues for our family forums and possibly for the first time in my life do exercise and get fit! I intend to become the complete opposite of who I was, a brand new Skilful Stacey"

Dad then commented.

"That's a very impressive and ambitious set of targets, and before the last week I would've considered it to be pure fantasy, but I no longer recognise my daughter and I've no idea what is possible. I'm still struggling to believe the change in you, but you already seem to be the complete opposite to the Stacey you've been as a teenager."

He got up and gave Stacey such a big hug he almost crushed her.

Stacey caught her breath and replied.

"But it's only been a week since my arrest and the only people who've seen my 'change' are you. If I am to be the new Stacey, I've got many many difficulties to overcome, my journey has actually barely begun."

Despite struggling to hold back her tears Nan commented.

"Can we make a date for next Christmas, to see how much has actually happened?"

Stacey immediately responded.

"Suzi and I have both written all this down in our diary or 'reflective log' as it is called these days so we can give a full report next year. We both felt that my 'change' was like Charles Dickens's 'Christmas Carol', but the story of Scrooge virtually ends just after Christmas, we both wanted to know what happened after that, particularly the following Christmas and to Tiny Tim. So we decided that we would try to update the story each Christmas. Next Christmas Suzi will have had her first term at secondary school and that will be a huge test for both of us, in fact all her teenage years will be a huge obstacle course for both of us, so we've got much to tell in future years. I also know I've got huge difficulties to overcome, and I must keep remembering 'the greater the difficulty the greater the success when I've overcome them'."

"Well I can't wait for next Christmas" said Gran.

"Nor me" said Nan.

"In my opinion this Christmas has been an incredible." Suzi suggested.

"Christmas began with a miracle and that's why we celebrate it, celebrating more miracles next year sounds ideal" Nan commented.

"A great comment Mum" said Dad "You never know, perhaps each Christmas we could have a series of sequels like 'Harry Potter, Lord of the Rings, or the Chronicles of Narnia'.

Nan continued and summed up everyone's feelings with this comment.

"Stacey, perhaps your story will copy the first Christmas, which was only just the start of a series of life changing events helping millions be able to live 'A Wonderful Life'."